9

Practice and Homework Book

Author Team
Nancy Anstett
Gordon Cooke
Catherine Heideman
Jim Mennie
Andrew Reeves

PEARSON
Education
Canada

Publisher
Claire Burnett

Publishing Team
Lynda Cowan
Jon Maxfield
Stephanie Kleven
Lynne Gulliver
Cheri Westra
Stephanie Cox
Judy Wilson

Design
Word & Image Design Studio Inc.

Typesetting
Computer Composition of Canada Inc.

Math Team Leader
Diane Wyman

Product Manager
Kathleen Crosbie

ISBN-13: 978-0-321-37328-1
ISBN-10:   0-321-37328-6

Printed and bound in Canada

4 5 -- WC -- 11

PEARSON
Education
Canada

Contents

About

Pearson Math 9 Practice and Homework Book

Welcome to *Pearson Math 9*. These pages describe how this Practice and Homework Book can support your progress through the year.

Each chapter offers the following features.

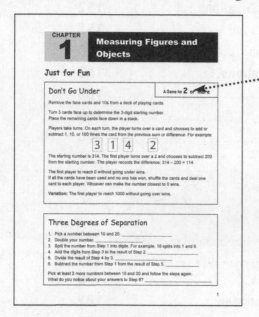

Just for Fun presents puzzles, games, or activities to help you warm up for the content to come. You may work with key words, numeracy skills, or creative and critical thinking skills.

For each lesson of the Student Book, the workbook usually provides 3 to 5 pages of support.

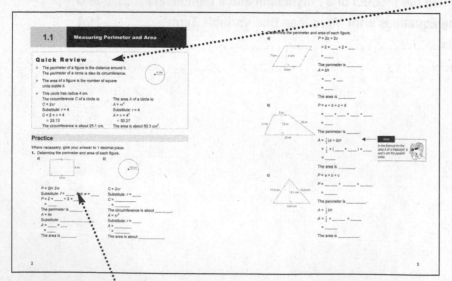

Quick Review covers the core concepts from the lesson. If used for homework, this Quick Review lets you bring just the Practice and Homework Book home.

Practice questions provide a structure for your work, gradually leaving more steps for you to complete on your own.

In Your Words helps to close off each chapter. This page identifies essential mathematical vocabulary from the chapter; gives one definition as an example, and allows you to record your understanding of other terms in your own words.

Chapter Review pages provide the same level of support as lesson Practice. Each Chapter Review question is referenced to the relevant lesson where related concepts are developed.

Tips and **Hints** point you in the right direction for success.

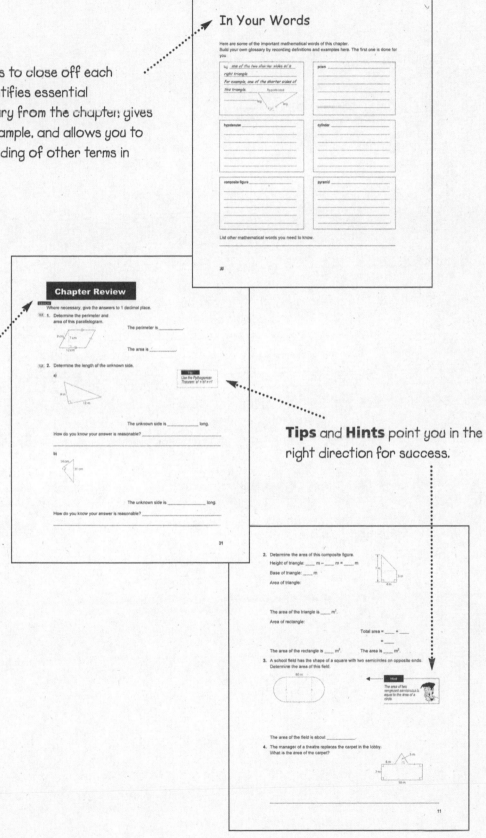

CHAPTER 1

Measuring Figures and Objects

Just for Fun

Don't Go Under

A Game for 2 or more

Remove the face cards and 10s from a deck of playing cards.

Turn 3 cards face up to determine the 3-digit starting number.
Place the remaining cards face down in a stack.

Players take turns. On each turn, the player turns over a card and chooses to add or subtract 1, 10, or 100 times the card from the previous sum or difference. For example:

$$\boxed{3} \quad \boxed{1} \quad \boxed{4} \qquad \boxed{2}$$

The starting number is 314. The first player turns over a 2 and chooses to subtract 200 from the starting number. The player records the difference: 314 − 200 = 114.

The first player to reach 0 without going under wins.
If all the cards have been used and no one has won, shuffle the cards and deal one card to each player. Whoever can make the number closest to 0 wins.

Variation: The first player to reach 1000 without going over wins.

Three Degrees of Separation

1. Pick a number between 10 and 20. _____
2. Double your number. _____
3. Split the number from Step 1 into digits. For example, 16 splits into 1 and 6.
4. Add the digits from Step 3 to the result of Step 2. _____
5. Divide the result of Step 4 by 3. _____
6. Subtract the number from Step 1 from the result of Step 5. _____

Pick at least 2 more numbers between 10 and 20 and follow the steps again.
What do you notice about your answers to Step 6? _____

1.1   Measuring Perimeter and Area

Practice

Where necessary, give your answer to 1 decimal place.

1. Determine the perimeter and area of each figure.

a)

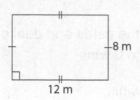

b)

$P = 2\ell + 2w$

Substitute: $\ell = $ _____ and $w = $ _____

$P = 2 \times $ _____ $+ 2 \times$ _____

   $= $ _____

The perimeter is _____.

$A = \ell w$

Substitute: _____

$A = $ _____ $\times$ _____

   $= $ _____

The area is _____.

$C = 2\pi r$

Substitute: $r = $ _____

$C = $ _____

   $\doteq $ _____

The circumference is about _____.

$A = \pi r^2$

Substitute: $r = $ _____

$A = $ _____

   $\doteq $ _____

The area is about _____.

2

2. Determine the perimeter and area of each figure.

a)

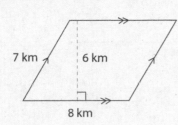

7 km   6 km

8 km

$P = 2b + 2c$

= 2 × ___ + 2 × ___

= ____

The perimeter is _____.

$A = bh$

= ___ × ___

= ____

The area is _____.

b)

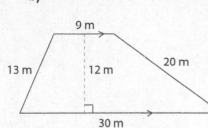

9 m

13 m   12 m   20 m

30 m

$P = a + b + c + d$

= ____ + ____ + ____ + ____

= ____

The perimeter is _____.

$A = \frac{1}{2}(a + b)h$

= $\frac{1}{2}$ × (____ + ____) × ____

= _____

The area is _____.

Hint

In the formula for the area A of a trapezoid, a and b are the parallel sides.

c)

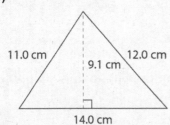

11.0 cm   9.1 cm   12.0 cm

14.0 cm

$P = a + b + c$

$P =$ _____ + _____ + _____

= _____

The perimeter is _____.

$A = \frac{1}{2}bh$

$A = \frac{1}{2}$ × _____ × _____

= _____

The area is _____.

3

3. Jeremy mows the front lawn of his house.
   The lawn has the shape of a trapezoid.
   What is the area that he mows?

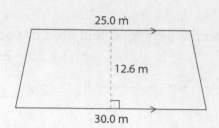

25.0 m

12.6 m

30.0 m

   The area he mows is _____.

4. a) A rectangle has a perimeter of 36 cm. Its width is 8 cm.
      What is its length?

   $P = 2\ell + 2w$

   Substitute: $P =$ _____ and $w =$ _____

   _____ $= 2\ell + 2($_____$)$

   Solve for ℓ.

   _____ $= 2\ell +$ _____

   $2\ell =$ _____

   $\ell =$ _____

   The rectangle is _____ long.

   b) A rectangle has an area of 45 m². Its length is 15 m.
      What is its width?

   $A = \ell w$

   Substitute: _____

   The rectangle is _____ wide.

4

5. Determine the perimeter and area of this semicircle.

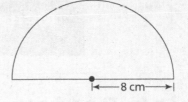

The perimeter of the semicircle is the sum of a straight length and a curved length.

The straight length is: 2 × _____ = _____

The curved length is one-half the circumference of a circle: $\frac{1}{2} \times 2\pi r = \pi r$

So, the curved length is: _____

P = _____ + _____ = _____

The perimeter is about _____.

$A = \frac{1}{2}\pi r^2$

$A = \frac{1}{2} \times \pi \times (\underline{\quad})^2$

$\doteq$ _____

The area is about _____.

> **Hint**
>
> The area of a semicircle is half the area of a circle.

6. Justine rides a carousel at the fair.
She sits on the edge of the carousel.
The carousel completes 7 turns while she rides it.
Determine the distance Justine travels.

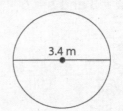

3.4 m

> **Hint**
>
> Determine the circumference of the circle. Then multiply by 7 to find the total distance.

7. The perimeter of a square window is 10 m. How long is each side of the window?

Quick Review

➢ In a right triangle, the shorter sides are the **legs**.
The longest side is opposite the right angle. It is called the **hypotenuse**.

➢ The Pythagorean Theorem is a relationship among the sides of a right triangle.
This relationship is written as:
$a^2 + b^2 = c^2$
The legs are a and b. The hypotenuse is c.

➢ To determine the hypotenuse in this
right triangle, substitute for a and b
in the formula $a^2 + b^2 = c^2$.
Substitute: $a = 3$ and $b = 5$

$$3^2 + 5^2 = c^2$$
$$9 + 25 = c^2$$
$$34 = c^2$$
$$c = \sqrt{34}$$
$$c \doteq 5.831$$

The hypotenuse is about 5.8 cm, to 1 decimal place.

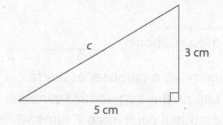

Practice

Where necessary, give your answer to 1 decimal place.

1. Determine the unknown length.

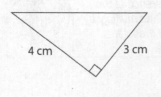

$$a^2 + b^2 = c^2$$
$$(\underline{\hspace{1cm}})^2 + (\underline{\hspace{1cm}})^2 = c^2$$
$$\underline{\hspace{1cm}} + \underline{\hspace{1cm}} = c^2$$
$$\underline{\hspace{1cm}} = c^2$$
$$c = \sqrt{}$$
$$c = \underline{\hspace{1cm}}$$

The hypotenuse is _____ cm.

Hint

Check your results.
Remember, the
hypotenuse is always
longer than the legs.

2. Determine each unknown length.

a)

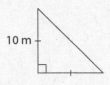

10 m

$a^2 + b^2 = c^2$

_____ + _____ $= c^2$

_____ $= c^2$

_____ $= c^2$

$c = \sqrt{}$

$c \doteq$ _____

The hypotenuse is about _____.

b)

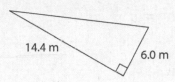

14.4 m

6.0 m

_____

3. Kiran goes down an inflatable slide at a carnival. How far does she slide?

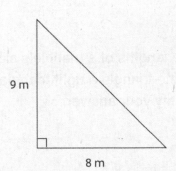

9 m

8 m

The length of the slide is _____.

7

4. Determine each unknown length.

a)

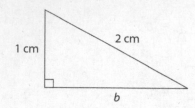

$a^2 + b^2 = c^2$

$(\underline{})^2 + b^2 = (\underline{})^2$

$\underline{} + b^2 = \underline{}$

$b^2 = \underline{} - \underline{}$

$b^2 = \underline{}$

$b = \sqrt{}$

$b \doteq \underline{}$

The length of the leg is about _____ cm.

b)

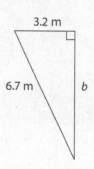

$a^2 + b^2 = c^2$

$b \doteq \underline{}$

The length of the leg is _____.

5. a) The lengths of a triangle's sides are 8 m, 6 m, and 10 m.
 Is the triangle a right triangle?
Justify your answer.

◄·········· | **Hint** |

The Pythagorean Theorem is only true for right triangles.

_____

b) The lengths of a triangle's sides are 7 cm, 9 cm, and 12 cm.
Is the triangle a right triangle? Justify your answer.

_____

6. A 2.6-m board forms a ramp that is 1.0 m
high at one end.
What is the horizontal length of the ramp?

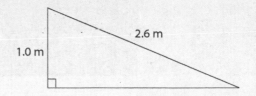

7. A floor tumble in gymnastics goes from one
corner of the square mat to the other.
What is the distance a gymnast travels while
tumbling?

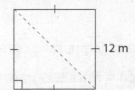

Quick Review

➤ A **composite figure** is a figure made up of other figures.

➤ This composite figure is made up of a triangle and a parallelogram.

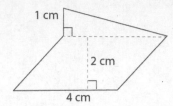

➤ Its area is the sum of the area of the parallelogram and the area of the triangle.

Area of parallelogram:

$A = bh$

$= 4 \times 2$

$= 8$

The area of the parallelogram is 8 cm^2.

Area of triangle:

$A = \frac{1}{2}bh$

$= \frac{1}{2} \times 4 \times 1$

$= 2$

The area of the triangle is 2 cm^2.

Total area = Parallelogram area + Triangle area

$= 8 + 2$

$= 10$

The area of the composite figure is 10 cm^2.

Practice

Where necessary, give your answer to 1 decimal place.

1. Determine the area of this composite figure.

Assume it is drawn on 1-cm grid paper.

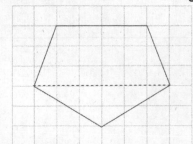

Total area = Trapezoid area + Triangle area

$= \underline{\hspace{1cm}} + \underline{\hspace{1cm}}$

$= \underline{\hspace{1cm}}$

The area is _____ cm^2.

Area of trapezoid:

$A = \frac{1}{2}(a + b)\,h$

$= \frac{1}{2} \times (\underline{\hspace{0.8cm}} + \underline{\hspace{0.8cm}}) \times \underline{\hspace{0.8cm}}$

$= \underline{\hspace{1cm}}$

The area of the trapezoid is _____ cm^2.

Area of triangle:

$A = \frac{1}{2}bh$

$= \underline{\hspace{1cm}}$

$= \underline{\hspace{1cm}}$

The area of the triangle is ___ cm^2.

2. Determine the area of this composite figure.

Height of triangle: _____ m – _____ m = _____ m

Base of triangle: _____ m

Area of triangle:

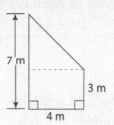

The area of the triangle is _____ m².

Area of rectangle:

Total area = _____ + _____

= _____

The area of the rectangle is _____ m².   The area is _____ m².

3. A school field has the shape of a square with two semicircles on opposite ends. Determine the area of this field.

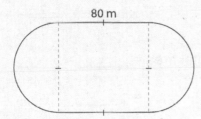

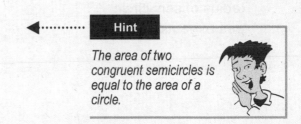

Hint

The area of two congruent semicircles is equal to the area of a circle.

The area of the field is about _____.

4. The manager of a theatre replaces the carpet in the lobby. What is the area of the carpet?

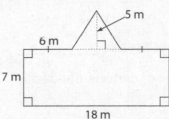

5. Determine the area of each composite figure.

a) Area of rectangle:

The area of the rectangle is _____.
Height of triangle: _____ cm
Base of triangle: _____ cm
Area of triangle:

$A =$ _____

   = _____

The area of the triangle is _____.

Draw a rectangle around this figure and label the leg lengths of the triangle.

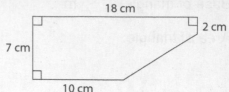

Total area = Rectangle area – Triangle area

       = _____ – _____

       = _____

The area is _____.

b) Area of trapezoid:

The area of the trapezoid is _____.
Radius of semicircle: _____
Area of semicircle:

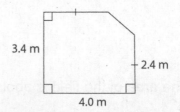

Total area = _____ – _____

       = _____

The area of the semicircle is _____.

The area is about _____.

6. Luis's mother wants to tile the floor of the mudroom. Each carton of floor tiles covers an area of 2.25 m². How many cartons should she order?

The floor area is _____.

Number of cartons needed:

She should order _____.

Quick Review

The perimeter of this composite figure is the sum of two sides of a triangle and one-half the circumference of a circle.

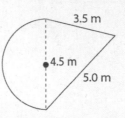

The diameter of the circle is 4.5 m.

The circumference of the circle is: $C = \pi d$

So, the circumference is: $C = \pi \times 4.5$

One-half the circumference is: $\frac{1}{2} \times \pi \times 4.5 \doteq 7.07$

The approximate perimeter of the composite figure is:
3.5 + 5.0 + 7.07 = 15.57

The perimeter is about 15.6 m.

Practice

Where necessary, give your answer to 1 decimal place.

1. Determine the perimeter of the composite figure.

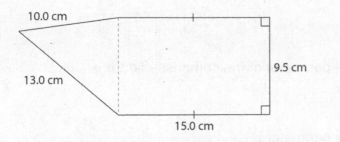

Its perimeter is the sum of _____ sides of a triangle and _____ sides of a rectangle.

_____ + _____ + _____ + _____ + _____ = _____

So, the perimeter of the composite figure is _____.

2. Determine the perimeter of each composite figure.

a)

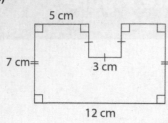

This figure has _____ sides.

The unknown length is: _____

The perimeter of the composite figure is:

The perimeter is _____.

b)

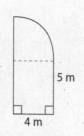

The perimeter of this figure is the sum of

_____ sides of a rectangle and one-quarter

the circumference of a circle.

The circumference of the circle is:

One-quarter the circumference is:

The perimeter of the composite figure is:

The perimeter is _____.

14

3. Determine the perimeter of each composite figure.
   Use the Pythagorean Theorem to determine the unknown length.

a)

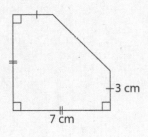

7 cm

3 cm

Triangle leg a: ____ – ____ = ____

Triangle leg b: ____ – ____ = ____

$$a^2 + b^2 = c^2$$

$$(\underline{\quad})^2 + (\underline{\quad})^2 = c^2$$

$$\underline{\quad} + \underline{\quad} = c^2$$

$$\underline{\quad} = c^2$$

$$c = \sqrt{\quad}$$

$$c \doteq \underline{\quad}$$

The approximate perimeter is:

The perimeter is about _____.

b)

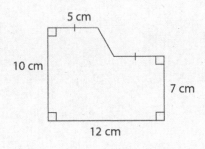

5 cm

10 cm

7 cm

12 cm

Triangle leg a: _____

Triangle leg b: _____

$$a^2 + b^2 = c^2$$

The approximate perimeter is:

The perimeter is about _____.

4. Jorge plays basketball in his driveway.
He draws the key of the basketball court using sidewalk chalk.
What is the perimeter of the key?

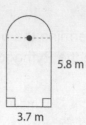

5.8 m

3.7 m

The perimeter is about _____.

5. Geraldine is replacing the baseboards around the bottom of the walls of a room.

a) What is the perimeter of the room?

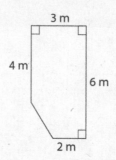

3 m

4 m

6 m

2 m

_____

b) Each baseboard is 2 m long. How many baseboards does Geraldine need?

_____

16

1.5   Volumes of a Prism and a Cylinder

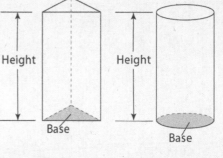

Quick Review

➤ The formula for the volume of a prism or a cylinder is:

V = base area × height

➤ The base of a cylinder is a circle with radius r.

The base area of a cylinder is: πr^2

So, the volume of a cylinder can also be written as: $V = \pi r^2 h$

You can use this formula to determine the volume of a cylinder with diameter 14 cm and height 20 cm.

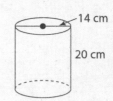

The radius is: $\frac{14 \text{ cm}}{2} = 7$ cm.

Substitute: $r = 7$ and $h = 20$

$V = \pi \times 7^2 \times 20$

$\doteq 3078.76$

The volume of the cylinder is about 3078.8 cm^3.

Practice

Where necessary, give your answer to 1 decimal place.

1. Determine the volume of each prism.

a)

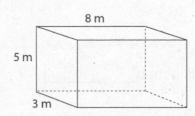

The base of this prism has the shape of a rectangle.

The area of a rectangle is: $A = \ell w$.

So, the volume of a rectangular prism is: $V = \ell w h$

Substitute: $\ell =$ ___, $w =$ ____, and $h =$ _____

$V =$ ____ × ____ × ____

   = _____

The volume is _____.

b)

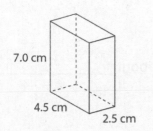

$V =$ _____

Substitute: _____

$V =$ _____

   = _____

The volume is about _____.

2. Determine the volume of each prism.

a)

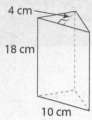

4 cm

18 cm

10 cm

The base of the prism has the shape of a triangle.

The base area is: $\frac{1}{2}$ × _____ × _____ = _____

The base area of the prism is _____ cm².

The volume of the prism is:

base area × height = _____ × _____

= _____

The volume of the prism is _____.

b)

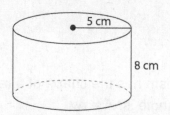

7.0 m

4.0 m

1.5 m

The base of the prism has

the shape of a _____.

The base area of the prism is _____.

The volume of the prism is _____.

3. Determine the volume of each cylinder.

a)

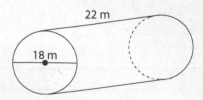

5 cm

8 cm

The volume of a cylinder is:

$V = \pi r^2 h$

Substitute: _____

$V = \pi \times ($ _____ $)^2 \times$ _____

≐ _____

The volume is about _____.

b)

22 m

18 m

The volume is about _____.

18

4. **a)** Fill in the missing labels in the sketch of the base of this prism.

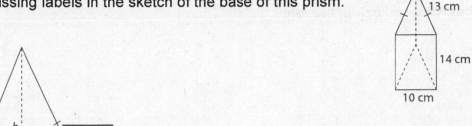

b) Determine the height of the base of this prism.
Use the Pythagorean Theorem.

$$h^2 + (\underline{\quad})^2 = (\underline{\quad})^2$$

$$h^2 + \underline{\quad} = \underline{\quad}$$

$$h^2 = \underline{\quad} - \underline{\quad}$$

$$h^2 = \underline{\quad}$$

$$h = \sqrt{\underline{\quad}}$$

$$h = \underline{\quad}$$

The height of the base is _____.

c) Determine the volume of the triangular prism.

The base area is: _____.

The volume is: base area × height = _____

= _____

The volume of the prism is _____.

5. Joon and Leon use a tent when they go camping.
   What is the volume of the tent?

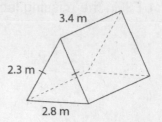

6. Kalen's Pool Services refills pools with water each spring.
   How much water will be needed for each pool? Assume each pool is filled to the top.

   a)

   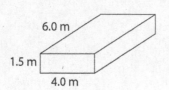

   _____

   _____

   b)

   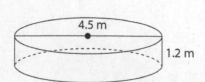

   _____

   _____

Quick Review

➤ A pyramid and prism with the same base and height are related.

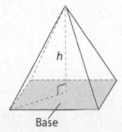

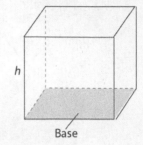

Base

Base

➤ The volume of a pyramid is one-third the volume of the related prism. So, the volume of the pyramid is:

$V = \frac{1}{3}Bh$

where B is the base area of the pyramid and h is the height of the pyramid.

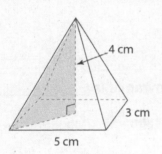

➤ The base of this pyramid is a rectangle measuring 5 cm by 3 cm. The base area is: $B = 5 \times 3 = 15$

The volume of the pyramid is $V = \frac{1}{3}Bh$

Substitute: $B = 15$ and $h = 4$

$V = \frac{1}{3} \times 15 \times 4 = 20$

The volume of the pyramid is 20 cm³.

Practice

Where necessary, give your answer to 1 decimal place.

1. Determine the volume of this pyramid.

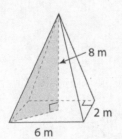

The base of the pyramid is a rectangle.

The area of the base is _____.

The volume of a pyramid is: $V = \frac{1}{3}Bh$

Substitute: $B =$ _____ and $h =$ _____

$V = \frac{1}{3} \times$ _____ $\times$ _____

$=$ _____

The volume of the pyramid is _____.

2. Determine the volume of each pyramid.
a) All edge lengths of this pyramid are 4.0 cm.
Each triangular face has height 3.5 cm.

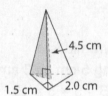

The base of the pyramid is a _____.

The area of the base is _____.

The volume of the pyramid is: $V = \frac{1}{3}Bh$

Substitute: $B =$ _____ and $h =$ _____

$V = \frac{1}{3} \times$ _____ $\times$ _____

$=$ _____

The volume of the pyramid is _____.

b) The base of this pyramid is a right triangle.

4.5 cm
1.5 cm   2.0 cm

The area of the base is _____.

The volume of the pyramid is _____.

3. The glass pyramid at the entrance to the Louvre is 20.6 m high.
The sides of its square base measure 35 m.

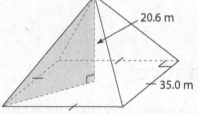

20.6 m
35.0 m

a) Determine the area of the base of the pyramid.

The area of the base is _____.

b) Determine the volume of the pyramid.

The volume of the pyramid is about _____.

4. A child's building block set has a triangular pyramid.
All edge lengths of the pyramid are 6.0 cm.
Determine the volume of wood in the block.

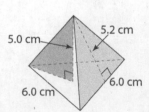

5.0 cm   5.2 cm
6.0 cm   6.0 cm

The volume of wood is _____.

5. This pyramid has a square base.

    a) What is the height of the pyramid?

        The height of the pyramid is
one leg of a right triangle.
The hypotenuse is
the height of a triangular face.
The other leg is one-half the base of the other triangular face.
Use the Pythagorean Theorem.

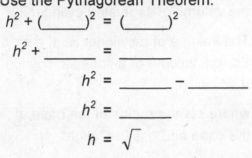

$$h^2 + (\underline{\hspace{1cm}})^2 = (\underline{\hspace{1cm}})^2$$

$$h^2 + \underline{\hspace{1.5cm}} = \underline{\hspace{1.5cm}}$$

$$h^2 = \underline{\hspace{1.5cm}} - \underline{\hspace{1.5cm}}$$

$$h^2 = \underline{\hspace{1.5cm}}$$

$$h = \sqrt{}$$

$$h = \underline{\hspace{1.5cm}}$$

◄ ·········· **Hint**

Use the Pythagorean Theorem to determine the height of the pyramid.

        The height of the pyramid is _____.

    b) What is the volume of the pyramid?

        Area of base: _____

        The volume of the pyramid is _____.

6. Henri makes large ice sculptures. He starts a sculpture by making an ice pyramid.
Its base is a square with side length 2.0 m.
The height of each triangular face is 2.4 m.

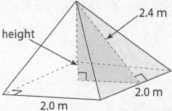

    a) Determine the height of the ice pyramid.

        The height of the pyramid is _____.

    b) Determine the volume of ice in the pyramid.

        The volume of ice is _____.

Quick Review

➢ A cylinder and cone with the same base and height are related.

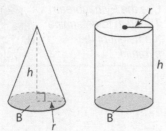

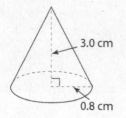

➢ The volume of a cone is one-third the volume of its related cylinder.

The volume of a cylinder is: $V = \pi r^2 h$
So, the volume of a cone is:
$V = \frac{1}{3}\pi r^2 h$

where r is the radius of the base of the cone and h is the height.

➢ The height of this cone is: $h = 3.0$
The radius of the base is: $r = 0.8$
The volume of the cone is: $V = \frac{1}{3}\pi r^2 h$
Substitute: $r = 0.8$ and $h = 3.0$
$V = \frac{1}{3} \times \pi \times 0.8^2 \times 3.0 \doteq 2.011$
The volume of the cone is about 2.0 cm^3.

Practice

Where necessary, give your answer to the nearest whole number.

1. Determine the volume of each cone.

a)

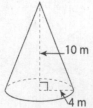

$V = \frac{1}{3}\pi r^2 h$

Substitute: $r =$ _____ and $h =$ _____.

$V = \frac{1}{3} \times \pi \times ($_____$)^2 \times$ _____

$\doteq$ _____

The volume of the cone is about _____ m^3.

b)

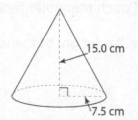

$V = \frac{1}{3}\pi r^2 h$

Substitute: _____.

$V =$ _____

$\doteq$ _____

The volume of the cone is
_____.

2. Determine the volume of each cone.

a)

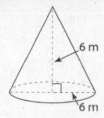

6 m

6 m

The radius of the cone is: $\dfrac{}{2}$ = _____

$V = \dfrac{1}{3}\pi r^2 h$

$ = \dfrac{1}{3} \times \pi \times (\underline{})^2 \times \underline{}$

$ \doteq \underline{}$

The volume of the cone is _____.

b)

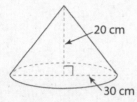

20 cm

30 cm

The radius of the cone is: _____

The volume of the cone is _____.

3. The base of this cone has diameter 10 cm.
The slant height is 13 cm.

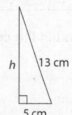

h 13 cm

10 cm

a) Determine the height of the cone.
The height of the cone is one leg of a right triangle.
The other leg is the radius of the cone.
The hypotenuse is the slant height.
Use the Pythagorean Theorem.

The radius is: _____

The slant height is: _____

$h^2 + (\underline{})^2 = (\underline{})^2$

$ h^2 + \underline{} = \underline{}$

$ h^2 = \underline{} - \underline{}$

$ h^2 = \underline{}$

$ h = \sqrt{}$

$ h = \underline{}$

The height h of the cone is _____.

13 cm

h

5 cm

b) Determine the volume of the cone.

$V = \dfrac{1}{3}\pi r^2 h$

$ = \dfrac{1}{3} \times \pi \times (\underline{})^2 \times \underline{}$

$ \doteq \underline{}$

The volume of the cone is _____.

4. The base of this cone has diameter 9 cm.
The slant height is 15 cm.

a) Determine the height of the cone to 1 decimal place.

The height of the cone is _____ .

b) Determine the volume of the cone.

The volume of the cone is _____ .

5. Liam dug a hole at the beach.
He piled the sand in 3 equal cones.
The diameter and slant height are shown for one cone.

a) Determine the height of the cone to 1 decimal place.

The height of the cone is _____ .

b) What is the volume of sand in the cone?

The volume of sand is _____ .

c) Liam wants to put the sand from all 3 cones in a cylindrical tub.
The tub has a diameter of 75 cm and a height of 40 cm.
Will all the sand fit in the tub without piling up over the rim?
Justify your answer without doing any calculations.

_____

_____

_____

_____

1.8 Volume of a Sphere

Quick Review

The volume of a sphere is two-thirds the volume of a cylinder into which the sphere fits exactly.

So, the volume V of a sphere with radius r is: $V = \frac{4}{3}\pi r^3$

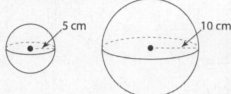

To determine the volume of the spheres, use the formula: $V = \frac{4}{3}\pi r^3$

1st sphere:
Substitute: $r = 5$

$V = \frac{4}{3} \times \pi \times 5^3$

$\doteq 523.599$

The volume is about 524 cm³.

2nd sphere:
Substitute: $r = 10$

$V = \frac{4}{3} \times \pi \times 10^3$

$\doteq 4188.790$

The volume is about 4189 cm³.

Practice

Give answers to the nearest whole number.

1. Determine the volume of each sphere.

a)

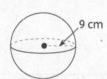

$V = \frac{4}{3}\pi r^3$

Substitute: $r =$ _____

$V = \frac{4}{3} \times \pi \times ($_____$)^3$

$\doteq$ _____

The volume of the sphere is about _____.

b)

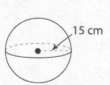

$V = \frac{4}{3}\pi r^3$

Substitute: _____

$V =$ _____

$\doteq$ _____

The volume of the sphere is about _____.

27

2. The height of this cylinder is twice its radius.
Label the sketch with the height of the cylinder.
Determine the volumes of the cylinder and the sphere.
The volume of a cylinder is: $V = \pi r^2 h$
The radius is: _____
The height is: 2 × _____ = _____
Substitute: r = _____ and h = _____
$V = \pi \times (\underline{\quad})^2 \times$ _____
 $\doteq$ _____
The volume of the can is about _____ m³.
The volume of a sphere is two-thirds the volume of the cylinder.

$V = \dfrac{2}{3} \times$ _____

 = _____
The volume of the sphere is about _____ m³.

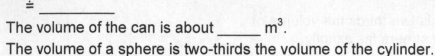

◄ ·········· Hint

Recall that the formula for the volume V of a cylinder is V = πr²h.

3. A solid rubber ball fits inside a can exactly.
The radius of the ball is 4 cm.

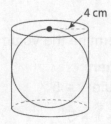

a) What is the volume of the can?

 The volume of the can is about _____.

b) What is the volume of the ball?

 The volume of the ball is about _____.

c) What is the volume of air in the can?

_____

4. Determine the volume of each sphere.

a)

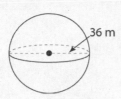

36 m

$V = \frac{4}{3}\pi r^3$

$r = \frac{\quad}{2} = $ _____

Substitute: $r = $ _____

$V = \frac{4}{3} \times \pi \times ($ _____ $)^3$

$\doteq$ _____

The volume of the sphere is about _____.

b)

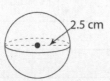

2.5 cm

$V = $ _____

$r = $ _____

Substitute: _____

$V = $ _____

$\doteq$ _____

The volume of the sphere is about _____.

5. The cafeteria is serving spaghetti and meatballs.
Each meatball is about 3.5 cm in diameter.
A serving has 5 meatballs.
What is the volume of meat in each serving?

Volume of 1 meatball:

Hint

First determine the volume of one meatball and then multiply that volume by 5.

Approximate volume of 5 meatballs:

The volume of meat in a serving is _____.

In Your Words

Here are some of the important mathematical words of this chapter.
Build your own glossary by recording definitions and examples here. The first one is done for you.

leg _one of the two shorter sides of a_
right triangle
For example, one of the shorter sides of
this triangle.

hypotenuse

leg

leg

prism _____

hypotenuse _____

cylinder _____

composite figure _____

pyramid _____

List other mathematical words you need to know.

_____

Chapter Review

LESSON

Where necessary, give the answers to 1 decimal place.

1.1 **1.** Determine the perimeter and area of this parallelogram.

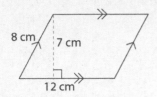

The perimeter is _____.

The area is _____.

1.2 **2.** Determine the length of the unknown side.

> **Tip**
>
> *Use the Pythagorean Theorem:* $a^2 + b^2 = c^2$

a)

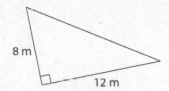

The unknown side is _____ long.

How do you know your answer is reasonable? _____

_____

b)

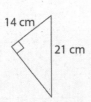

The unknown side is _____ long.

How do you know your answer is reasonable? _____

_____

3. The town parks department is laying sod in two parts of a new park.
Determine the area of sod that each part needs.

a)

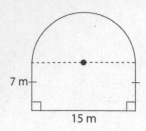

The area of sod needed is _____.

b)

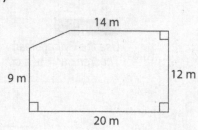

The area of sod needed is _____.

4. The town parks department is putting a brick border around each part of the park in
question 3. Determine the length of border that each part needs.

a)   b)

The length of border needed for   The length of border needed for the
the first park is _____.   second park is _____.

5. Determine the volume of each solid.

a)

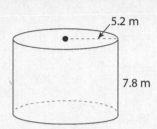

5.2 m

7.8 m

The volume of the cylinder is _____.

b)

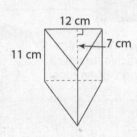

12 cm

7 cm

11 cm

The volume of the triangular prism is _____.

6. Determine the volume of each pyramid.

a)

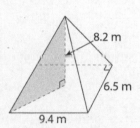

8.2 m

6.5 m

9.4 m

The volume of the rectangular pyramid

is about _____.

b)

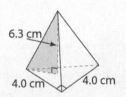

6.3 cm

4.0 cm   4.0 cm

The volume of the triangular pyramid

is _____.

7. A pile of salt is a cone. Determine the volume of salt.

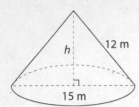

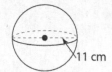

Hint

Use the Pythagorean Theorem to determine the height of the cone

The height of the cone is about _____.

The volume of the salt is about _____.

8. This glass marble is a sphere. What is the volume of glass in the marble?

The volume of glass in the marble is about _____.

Just for Fun

Rectangle Relationships

Draw a rectangle that has perimeter 12 cm.
Label the length, width, and area of the rectangle.

Draw a different rectangle that also has perimeter 12 cm.

Do the rectangles have the same area?

_____

_____

Rearrange Rectangles

A   B   C   D   E

Can you arrange rectangles **A**, **B**, **C**, and **D** to make rectangle **E**? Why or why not?

_____

_____

Quick Review

➤ Suppose you saw a board that is
60 cm long into two pieces.
The lengths of the two pieces can vary,
but their sum is always 60 cm.

40 cm	20 cm

50 cm	10 cm

30 cm	30 cm

➤ The formula for the area of a rectangle is:

$A = \ell w$

➤ The formula for the perimeter of a rectangle is: $P = 2\ell + 2w$
The perimeter of a rectangle is twice the sum of its length and width.

The perimeter of a rectangle is 16 cm.
So, the sum of its length and width is 8 cm.
$\ell + w = 8$

Practice

Where necessary, give the answers to 1 decimal place.

1. Point M moves along a line segment.

A   ← M →   B

   a) Which measures vary?
   The lengths of line segments _____ and _____ vary.

   b) Which measure stays the same?

   _____

2. This rectangle has length 46 mm and width 30 mm.

46 mm

30 mm

a) Determine the perimeter and area of the rectangle.

$P = 2\ell + 2w$

$P = 2(\underline{\hspace{1cm}}) + 2(\underline{\hspace{1cm}}) = \underline{\hspace{1cm}}$

The perimeter is _____.

$A = \ell w$

$A = \underline{\hspace{1cm}} \times \underline{\hspace{1cm}} = \underline{\hspace{1cm}}$

The area is _____.

b) Suppose the length increases by 4 mm and the width decreases by 4 mm.
Calculate the new perimeter and area.

The new length is _____.

The new width is _____.

The perimeter is _____.

The area is _____.

c) Suppose the length of the rectangle in part a triples and the width is divided by 3.
Calculate the new perimeter and area.

The perimeter is _____.

The area is _____.

3. a) Sketch 2 different rectangles with perimeter 14 units.
The sum of the length and width of each rectangle is _____ units.
Label each rectangle with its dimensions.

b) Sketch 2 different rectangles with area 12 square units.
The product of the length and width of each triangle is _____ square units.
Label each rectangle with its dimensions.

4. Jane wants to make a rectangular pen for her dog. She has 18 m of fence.

   a) Determine the length and width of three possible pens.

   The perimeter is 18 m. ◀ ⋯⋯⋯⋯

   So, the sum of the length and width is _____ m.

   $\ell + w =$ _____

> **Hint**
>
> The perimeter of a rectangle is twice the sum of its length and width.

Width (m)	Length (m)	Perimeter (m)

   b) Sketch each pen.

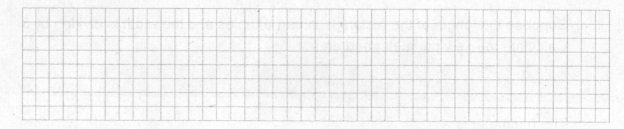

5. A rectangle has area 18 m². ◀ ⋯⋯⋯⋯

   Determine 3 different lengths and widths for the rectangle.

> **Hint**
>
> The area of a rectangle is the product of its length and width.

Width (m)	Length (m)	Area (m²)

Rectangles with Given Perimeter or Area

Quick Review

➤ Rectangles with the same perimeter can have different areas

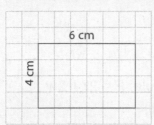

To compare the areas of these rectangles, use the formula: $A = \ell w$

1st Rectangle
Substitute: $\ell = 6$ and $w = 4$
$A = 6 \times 4$
$\quad = 24$
The area is 24 cm^2.

2nd Rectangle
Substitute: $\ell = 7$ and $w = 3$
$A = 7 \times 3$
$\quad = 21$
The area is 21 cm^2.

These rectangles have the same perimeter but different areas.

➤ Rectangles with the same area can have different perimeters.

Compare the perimeters of the rectangles.
Use the formula: $P = 2\ell + 2w$

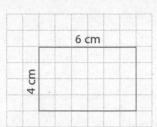
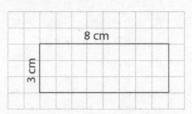

1st Rectangle
Substitute: $\ell = 6$ and $w = 4$
$P = 2(6) + 2(4)$
$\quad = 12 + 8$
$\quad = 20$
The perimeter is 20 cm.

2nd Rectangle
Substitute: $\ell = 8$ and $w = 3$
$P = 2(8) + 2(3)$
$\quad = 16 + 6$
$\quad = 22$
The perimeter is 22 cm.

These rectangles have the same area but different perimeters.

Practice

Where necessary, give the answers to 1 decimal place.

1. a) Draw each rectangle on the grid below.
   Assume each square in the grid has side length 1 cm.

   i) $\ell = 2$, $w = 5$ ii) $\ell = 4$, $w = 3$ iii) $\ell = 6$, $w = 2$

   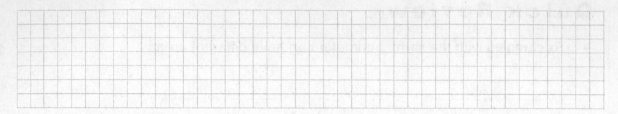

   b) Which rectangles have the same perimeter? Use the formula: $P = 2\ell + 2w$

   i) $P = 2(\underline{\quad}) + 2(\underline{\quad})$ ii) $P = \underline{\hspace{3cm}}$ iii)

        $= \underline{\quad}$ $= \underline{\hspace{3cm}}$

   The perimeter is _____ cm.   The perimeter is _____.   _____

   _____

   c) Which rectangles have the same area? Use the formula: $A = \ell w$

   i) $A = \underline{\quad} \times \underline{\quad}$ ii) $A = \underline{\hspace{3cm}}$ iii)

        $= \underline{\quad}$ $= \underline{\hspace{3cm}}$

   The area is _____.   The area is _____.   _____

   _____

2. a) Draw 2 more rectangles with the same perimeter as this rectangle.

   b) Assume each square in the grid above has side length 1 cm.
   Calculate the area of each rectangle. Use the formula: _____

   The area is _____ cm².   The area is _____.   _____

   c) Describe how the shapes of the rectangles change as the area increases.

   _____

3. **a)** Draw a square with side length 4 units.
Calculate its perimeter and area.

The perimeter is _____.

The area is _____.

b) Draw a rectangle that has the same perimeter as the square in part a.
Calculate its area.

The area is _____.

c) Which figure has the greater area?

_____

4. Kerri is placing brick edging around the perimeter of 2 rectangular lawns.

a) Calculate the perimeter and area of each lawn.

1st Lawn

30 m

20 m

2nd Lawn

40 m

15 m

The perimeter is _____ m.

The perimeter is _____.

b) Which lawn has the greater perimeter?

_____

Quick Review

➤ The maximum area of a rectangle with a given perimeter occurs when the length and width are closest in value.

The perimeter of a rectangle is 14 cm.
Each dimension is a whole number of centimetres.

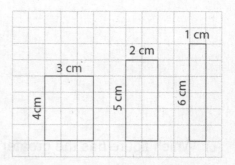

Width (cm)	Length (cm)	Area (cm^2)
1	6	6
2	5	10
3	4	12

From the table, the maximum area is 12 cm^2.
The rectangle with the maximum area has dimensions
closest in value: 3 cm and 4 cm.

➤ Among all rectangles with a given perimeter,
a square has the maximum area.
A square with perimeter 14 cm has side length 3.5 cm.
Its area is 12.25 cm^2.

Practice

1. **a)** Sketch three rectangles with perimeter 12 cm.
    Each dimension is a whole number of centimetres.
    Label each rectangle with its dimensions and area.

   b) Which rectangle has the maximum area?

_____

2. Payam is using 1-m blocks of wood to build a rectangular garden.
There are 18 blocks of wood, and they cannot be cut.

a) Sketch the possible gardens that can be enclosed by the blocks of wood.
Label each garden with its dimensions.

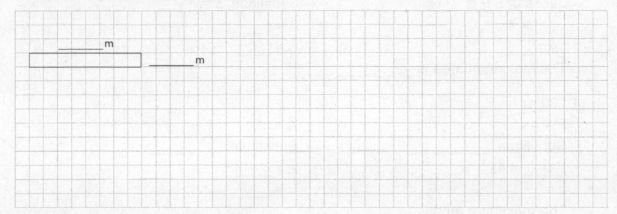

b) Calculate the area of each garden.

Width (m)	Length (m)	Area (m^2)
1	8	

c) What are the dimensions of the garden with the maximum area?

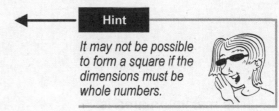

Hint

It may not be possible to form a square if the dimensions must be whole numbers.

_____

d) Is the garden with maximum area a square? Explain.

_____

3. Determine the maximum area for a rectangle with each perimeter.

a) 40 m

The maximum area occurs when the rectangle is a square.

$P = 4s$ $A = s^2$

Substitute: $P =$ _____   Substitute: $s =$ _____

_____ $= 4s$ $A = ($ _____ $)^2$

$s =$ _____ $=$ _____

The maximum area is _____.

b) 100 m

$P = 4s$ $A = s^2$

Substitute: _____   Substitute: _____

_____ $= 4s$ $A =$ _____

$s =$ _____ $=$ _____

The maximum area is _____.

c) 60 m

$s =$ _____

Hint

First determine the side length s of a square using the perimeter.

$A =$ _____

The maximum area is _____.

d) 88 m

The maximum area is _____.

4. Mario is cutting an opening in a bathroom ceiling for an air diffuser. The perimeter of the opening will be 48 cm.

a) What dimensions will give the greatest area?

_____

b) What is the maximum possible area? _____

Quick Review

➤ The minimum perimeter of a rectangle occurs
  when the length and width are closest in value.

➤ The area of a rectangle is 24 cm^2.
  Each dimension is a whole number of centimetres.

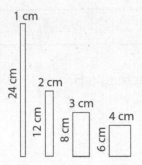

Width (cm)	Length (cm)	Perimeter (cm)
1	24	50
2	12	28
3	8	22
4	6	20

From the table, the minimum perimeter is 20 cm.
The rectangle with the minimum perimeter has
dimensions closest in value: 4 cm and 6 cm.

➤ Among all rectangles with a given area,
  a square has the minimum perimeter.
  A square with area 24 cm^2 has side length about 4.9 cm.
  Its perimeter is 19.6 cm.

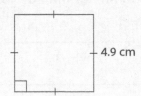

4.9 cm

Practice

Where necessary, round your answers to 1 decimal place.

1. **a)** Draw a different rectangle that has the same area as Rectangle A.

    b) Do the two rectangles have the same perimeter? Explain.

_____

_____

2. **a)** Draw 2 different rectangles that have the same area as Rectangle B.
Each side should be a whole number of grid units.

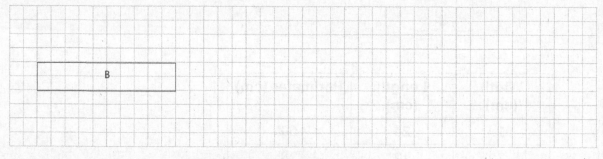

    b) Label the length, width, and perimeter of each rectangle.

    c) Which rectangle has the minimum perimeter?

_____

    d) Is it possible to form a rectangle with a lesser
perimeter than the one in part c? Explain.

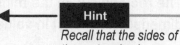

> **Hint**
> Recall that the sides of
> the rectangles in
> question 2a are
> restricted to whole
> numbers.

_____

_____

3. a) Draw a rectangle that has the same area as Rectangle E with the minimum perimeter.

b) Label the rectangle's length, width, and perimeter.

c) Do the 2 rectangles have the same perimeter? Explain.

_____

4. What is the minimum perimeter for a rectangle with each area?

a) 121 cm^2

The minimum perimeter occurs when the rectangle is a square.

$A = s^2$ $P = 4s$

Substitute: $A =$ _____   Substitute: $s =$ _____

_____ $= s^2$ $P = 4(\underline{})$

$s = \sqrt{}$ $=$ _____

$s =$ _____

The minimum perimeter is _____ cm.

> **Tip**
> You can use the $\sqrt{}$ button on a calculator to determine the square root of a number.

b) 225 cm^2

The minimum perimeter occurs when the rectangle is a _____.

$A =$ _____ $P =$ _____

Substitute: $A =$ _____   Substitute: _____

                                                      $P =$ _____

                                                      $=$ _____

$s =$ _____

The minimum perimeter is _____.

5. Tony's construction company is pouring concrete patios.
Determine the minimum perimeter of a patio with each area.
Show your work.

a) 16 m^2

$A =$ _____ $P =$ _____

Substitute: _____   Substitute: _____

The perimeter is _____.

b) 25 m^2

_____

c) 35 m^2

_____

Quick Review

➤ Jim is building a flowerbed along
the side of his house.
He has 11 m of edging to put along
the other three sides of the flowerbed.
The edging comes in 1-m pieces.
What is the maximum area of the flowerbed?

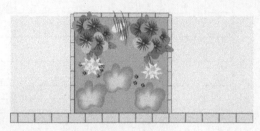

Make a table to determine the widths and lengths of possible flowerbeds.

Width (m)	Length (m)	Area (m²)
1	9	9
2	7	14
3	5	15
4	3	12
5	1	5

Consider a flowerbed with width 1 m.
The edging forms two widths and
one length of the flowerbed.
There is 11 m of edging.
Two widths are: 2(1 m) = 2 m
So, the length is: 11 m – 2 m = 9 m
The area is: (1 m)(9 m) = 9 m²

The maximum flowerbed area is not a square.
It is a rectangle that measures 3 m by 5 m.

Practice

1. a) A banner 12 m long is draped around 3 sides of a rectangular display.
The other side of the display is against the wall.
Label the missing measures on these rectangles. The first one is done for you.
Circle the rectangle with the largest area.

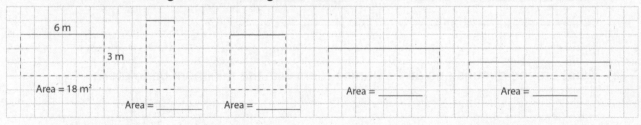

6 m

3 m

Area = 18 m²

Area = _____

Area = _____

Area = _____

Area = _____

b) How are the length and width of the maximum area for the display related?

_____

2. Cindy is building a deck on one side of her house.
She has 14 pieces of 1-m railing to put around the deck.

a) Complete the table to determine possible widths and lengths for the deck.
Each side of the deck should be a whole number of metres.

Width (m)	Length (m)	Area (m^2)
1	12	
2		

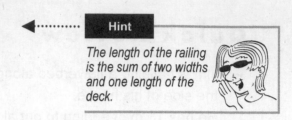

Hint

The length of the railing is the sum of two widths and one length of the deck.

b) What dimensions give the maximum area for the deck?

_____

_____

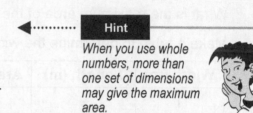

Hint

When you use whole numbers, more than one set of dimensions may give the maximum area.

3. Mil is building a games room with walls on three sides in his basement.
He wants the floor area to be 24 m^2.

a) List pairs of measures whose product is 24.

Width (m)	Length (m)	Perimeter (m)
1		
2		

b) What are the dimensions of the games room with the minimum perimeter?

_____

_____

4. Tina has 18 square patio stones that each have side length 1 m.
The patio is to be built against the side of a house.
Tina will then put edging on 3 sides.

a) List pairs of measures with product 18.

Width (m)	Length (m)	Area (m^2)
1	18	

b) Calculate the edging
required for each patio.

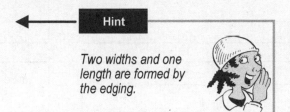

Hint

*Two widths and one
length are formed by
the edging.*

c) Draw the patios on the grid.
Use a solid line to represent the side of the house
and a dashed line to represent the edging.
Label each patio with its dimensions.

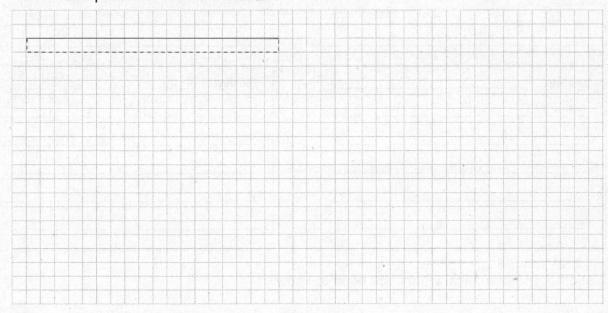

d) Circle the patio that requires the minimum edging.

In Your Words

Here are some of the important mathematical words of this chapter.
Build your own glossary by recording definitions and examples here. The first one is done for you.

maximum _greatest_
For example, the maximum of 3, 4, and
_5 is 5._

area _____

minimum _____

whole number _____

perimeter _____

congruent _____

List other mathematical words you need to know.

_____

Chapter Review

Where necessary, give the answers to 1 decimal place.

2.1 1. Vincent is making rectangles out of 20 wooden tiles from a board game.
He stands the tiles on their sides to make the rectangles.
The tiles are square and each has side length 1 cm.
Determine the length of the rectangle for each width.

Width (cm)	Length (cm)	Perimeter (cm)
1		
2		
3		
4		
5		

2.2 2. A rectangle has perimeter 30 cm.

a) For each width, determine the length and area of the rectangle.

Width (cm)	Length (cm)	Area (cm^2)
1		
3		
4		
5		
6		
7		

b) What happens to the area as the width and length get closer in value?

_____

3. A rectangle has area 36 m^2.

   a) For each width, determine the length and perimeter of the rectangle.

Width (m)	Length (m)	Perimeter (m)
1		
2		
3		
4		
6		

   b) What happens to the area as the width and length get closer in value?

   _____

4. Jarratt has 24 m of fencing for a rectangular garden.
   The fencing comes in 1-m sections that cannot be cut.

   a) Sketch the possible gardens.
   Label each garden with its dimensions.

   b) Calculate the area of each garden in part a.
   Label each garden with its area.

   c) Which garden has the maximum area?

   _____

5. a) Determine the dimensions of the rectangle with the maximum area.

i) $P = 12$ cm

$P = 4s$

Substitute: $P = $ ____

____ $= 4s$

$s = $ ____

The rectangle is a square with side length ____ cm.

ii) $P = 18$ cm

$P = $ ____

Substitute: _____

$s = $ _____

The rectangle is a square with side length _____.

iii) $P = 33.2$ cm

_____

_____

_____

b) Calculate the area of each rectangle in part a.

i) $A = s^2$

Substitute: $s = $ ____

$A = ($ ____ $)^2$

$= $ ____

The maximum area is ____ cm^2.

ii) $A = $ _____

Substitute: _____

$A = $ _____

$\doteq$ _____

The maximum area is about _____.

iii)

_____

_____

_____

2.4 **6.** Determine the minimum perimeter for each area.

a) $A = 25$ cm^2

$A = s^2$

Substitute: $A = $ ____

____ $= s^2$

$s = \sqrt{}$

$s = $ ____

$P = 4s$

Substitute: $s = $ ____

$P = 4($ ____ $)$

$= $ ____

The minimum perimeter is _____.

b) $A = 64$ cm^2

$A = $ ____

Substitute: $A = $ ____

$s = $ ____

$P = $ ____

Substitute: _____

$P = $ ____

$= $ ____

The minimum perimeter is _____.

c) $A = 120$ cm^2

7. A rectangular sheep pen is enclosed by 20 m of fencing.

a) What dimensions give the maximum area for the pen?

The maximum area occurs when _____

_____

P = 20 m

pen

The sheep pen with maximum area measures _____ m by _____ m.

b) Suppose the pen is next to a river.
Complete the table. What dimensions give the maximum area for the field?

Two widths and one length are formed by the fence.

The length of the fence is _____.

P = 20 m

pen

river

Width (m)	Length (m)	Area (m²)
1	18	18

The sheep pen with maximum area measures _____ by _____.

The maximum area occurs when _____

56

Relationships in Geometry

Just for Fun

Half Way

Take a piece of paper.
Fold it exactly in half.

Unfold the paper.
Fold it exactly in half a different way.

Unfold the paper.
Fold it exactly in half another way.

What did you notice about the fold lines?

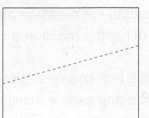

_____

Name That Polygon

Polygons have names based on Greek words.
Use a reference text or the Internet to complete the table.

Number of Sides	Name of Polygon
6	
	heptagon
8	
	nonagon
10	
12	
20	
	hectogon
10 000	

Quick Review

➤ The 3 angles in a triangle are its interior angles.
The sum of the angles in a triangle is 180°.
That is, $a + b + c = 180°$

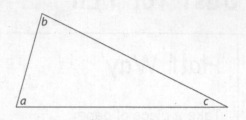

➤ You can calculate the measure of an unknown angle
in a triangle using the measures of the other 2 angles.

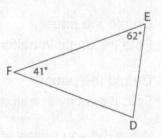

The sum of the two known angles is: 62° + 41° = 103°
The sum of the angles in a triangle is 180°.
Subtract to determine ∠D: 180° − 103° = 77°
So, ∠D = 77°

Practice

1. Determine each unknown angle.

a)

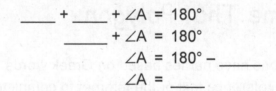

_____ + _____ + ∠A = 180°

_____ + ∠A = 180°

∠A = 180° − _____

∠A = _____

b)

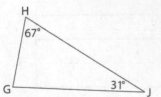

_____ + _____ + ∠K = _____

_____ + ∠K = _____

∠K = _____ − _____

∠K = _____

c)

∠G = _____

2. Determine the unknown angle in each right triangle.

a)

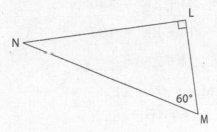

_____ + _____ + ∠N = 180°

_____ + ∠N = 180°

∠N = 180° − _____

∠N = _____

b)

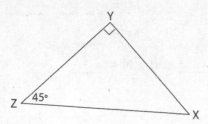

_____ + _____ + ∠X = _____

_____ + ∠X = _____

∠X = _____ − _____

∠X = _____

c)

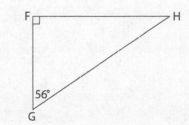

∠H = _____

3. What is the sum of the 2 acute angles in any right triangle?

_____

4. Determine the unknown
angle measures
in each isosceles triangle.

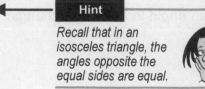

Hint

*Recall that in an
isosceles triangle, the
angles opposite the
equal sides are equal.*

a)

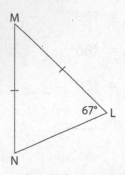

_____ + ∠M + ∠N = 180°

∠M + ∠N = 180° – _____

∠M + ∠N = _____

NM = LM, so ∠N = ∠L

∠L = _____, so ∠N = _____

∠M + _____ = _____

∠M = _____ – _____

∠M = _____

∠M = _____ and ∠N = _____

b)

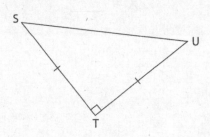

5. For each set of angles, can a triangle be drawn?

Justify your answers.

a) 30°, 60°, 90°

_____

b) 80°, 80°, 80°

_____

3.2   Exterior Angles of a Triangle

Quick Review

- ➤ To draw an exterior angle of a triangle, extend 1 side of the triangle.

- ➤ An exterior angle of a triangle is equal to the sum of the 2 opposite interior angles. That is, $e = a + b$

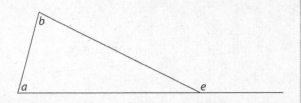

- ➤ You can use this relationship to calculate the measure of an unknown angle.

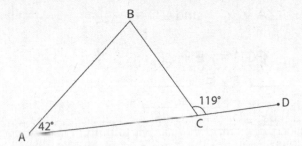

$\angle BCD = \angle A + \angle B$
So, $119° = 42° + \angle B$
$119° - 42° = 77°$

So, $\angle B = 77°$

- ➤ The sum of the 3 exterior angles of any triangle is 360°. That is, $p + q + r = 360°$

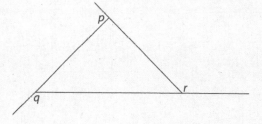

Practice

1. Determine each unknown exterior angle.

a)

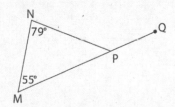

$\angle NPQ = 79° + \underline{\hspace{1cm}}$
$= \underline{\hspace{1cm}}$

b)

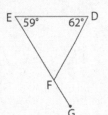

$\angle DFG = \underline{\hspace{1cm}} + \underline{\hspace{1cm}}$
$= \underline{\hspace{1cm}}$

c)

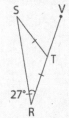

$\angle STV = \underline{\hspace{1cm}} + \underline{\hspace{1cm}}$
$= \underline{\hspace{1cm}}$

61

2. Determine the unknown interior angles.

← **Hint**

If you know an exterior angle, you can subtract 1 of the opposite interior angles to determine the other opposite interior angle.

a)

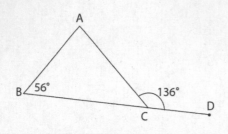

$\angle ACD = \angle A + \angle B$

$136° = \angle A +$ ____

$136° -$ ____ $=$ ____

$\angle A =$ ____

____ $+ \angle C = 180°$

$\angle C = 180° -$ ____

$\angle C =$ ____

$\angle A =$ ____ and $\angle C =$ ____

b)

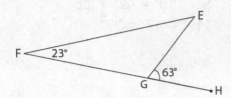

$\angle EGH = \angle E + \angle F$

____ $= \angle E +$ ____

____ $-$ ____ $=$ ____

$\angle E =$ ____

____ $+ \angle G =$ ____

$\angle G =$ ____ $-$ ____

$\angle G =$ ____

$\angle E =$ ____ and $\angle G =$ ____

c)

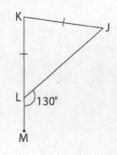

3. Use the diagram to determine relationships among the angles.

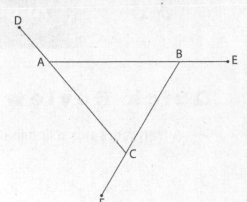

a) What angle has the same measure as ∠A + ∠B?

_____

b) What angle has the same measure as ∠DAB − ∠B?

_____

c) Name 3 angles whose sum is 180°.

_____

d) Name 3 angles whose sum is 360°.

_____

4. This sail has been ripped and must be patched.
It was made by sewing together 4 triangular panels.
Determine the measure of the angle that is
missing from each panel.

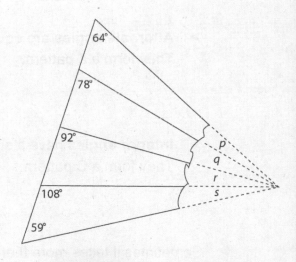

Hint

*The interior angle of
108° in the bottom
triangle is an exterior
angle of the triangle
above it.*

Quick Review

➢ A **transversal** is a line that intersects 2 or more other lines.

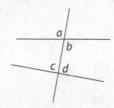

➢ Opposite angles are equal.
    a and *b* are opposite angles.

➢ Straight angles measure 180°.
    c and *d* form a straight angle.

➢ When a transversal intersects parallel lines, more pairs of angles are related.

➢ **Corresponding angles** are equal.
They form an F pattern.

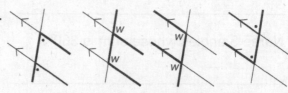

➢ **Alternate angles** are equal.
They form a Z pattern.

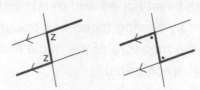

➢ **Interior angles** have a sum of 180°.
They form a C pattern.

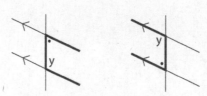

➢ Sometimes it takes more than one step to determine the measure of an angle.

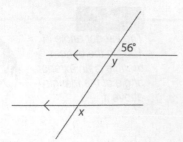

y and 56° form a straight angle.
The sum of their measures is 180°.
$y = 180° - 56°$
   $= 124°$

y and *x* are corresponding angles.
They are equal.
$y = 124°$, so $x = 124°$.

Practice

1. Determine the angle measure indicated by each letter.

a)

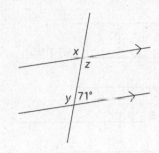

z and 71° form a ____ pattern.

So, they are _____ angles.

They have a sum of _____.

$z + 71° = $ _____

$z = $ _____ $- 71°$

$z = $ _____

z and x are _____ angles.

Their measures are _____.

$z = $ _____, so $x = $ _____

y and 71° form a _____.

They have a sum of _____.

So, $y = $ _____ $-$ ____

= _____

$x = $ _____, $y = $ _____, and $z = $ _____

w and 88° form a _____.

They have a sum of _____.

b)

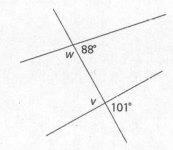

$w \doteq $ _____

v and 101° are _____ angles.

They are _____.

So, $v = $ _____

2. Determine the angle measure indicated by each letter.
Which relationships did you use?

a)

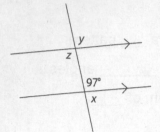

y and 97° are _____ angles.

y = _____

z and 97° are _____ angles.

z = _____

x and 97° form a _____.

x = _____

b)

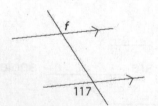

m and 50° are _____ angles.

m = _____

m and n are _____ angles.

n = _____

n and p form a _____.

p = _____

3. Determine the angle measure indicated by each letter.

Hint

Look for corresponding, alternate, and interior angles in the diagrams.

a)

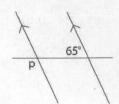

f

117

f = _____

b)

p

65°

p = _____

4. Determine the angle measure indicated by each letter.

a)

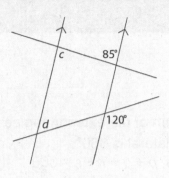

_c_ and 85° are _____ angles.

_c_ = _____

Find an angle on the diagram that is related to _d_ and to the angle marked 120°. Label that angle _e_.

_e_ and 120° _____.

_e_ = _____

_d_ and _e_ _____.

_d_ = _____

b)

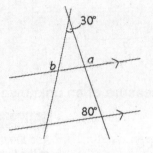

Find the angle in the small triangle that is related to _a_ and to the angle marked 80°. Label that angle _c_.

_c_ = _____

_a_ = _____

_b_ is an exterior angle of the triangle.

> **Tip**
>
> _Remember: An exterior angle of a triangle is equal to the sum of the two opposite interior angles._

_b_ = _____

c)

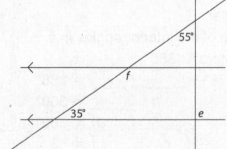

Quick Review

➤ The sum of the interior angles of a quadrilateral is 360°.
That is, $a + b + c + d = 360°$

➤ The sum of the exterior angles of a quadrilateral is 360°.
That is, $p + q + r + s = 360°$

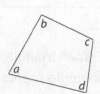

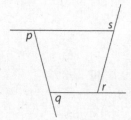

➤ You can use these relationships to determine the measure of an unknown angle when you know the other three angles.

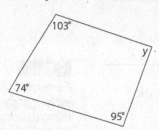

$$y + 103° + 74° + 95° = 360°$$
$$y + 272° = 360°$$
$$y = 360° - 272°$$
$$y = 88°$$

So, angle y measures 88°

Tip

Add the measures of the three known interior angles. Subtract the sum from 360°.

Practice

1. Determine the angle measure indicated by each letter.

a)

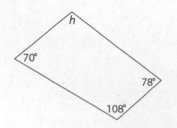

The sum of the interior angles in a quadrilateral is 360°.

So, $h + 78° + $ _____ $ + $ _____ $ = 360°$
$$h + \text{\_\_\_\_\_} = 360°$$
$$h = 360° - \text{\_\_\_\_\_}$$
$$h = \text{\_\_\_\_\_}$$

b)

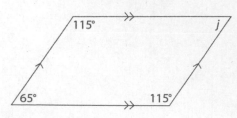

The sum of the interior angles in a parallelogram is _____.

$$j + \text{\_\_\_\_} + \text{\_\_\_\_\_} + \text{\_\_\_\_\_} = \text{\_\_\_\_\_}$$
$$j + \text{\_\_\_\_\_} = \text{\_\_\_\_\_}$$
$$j = \text{\_\_\_\_\_} - \text{\_\_\_\_}$$
$$j = \text{\_\_\_\_}$$

2. Determine the angle measure indicated by each letter.

a)

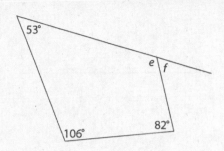

$e +$ ____ $+$ ____ $+$ ____ $=$ ____

$e +$ ____ $=$ ____

$e =$ ____ $-$ ____

$e =$ ____

e and f form a _____.

So, $e + f =$ ____

Substitute: $e =$ ____

____ $+ f = 180°$

$f = 180° -$ ____

$f =$ ____

b)

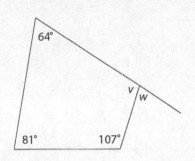

$v =$ _____

v and w form a _____.

So, _____

Substitute: _____

____ $+ w =$ ____

$w =$ ____ $-$ ____

$w =$ ____

3. Determine the angle measure indicated by each letter.

Draw a diagonal on the kite to form two congruent triangles.

How are b and 122° related?

_____

_____

$b =$ ____

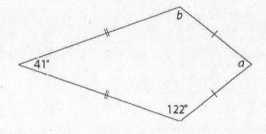

$a =$ ____

69

4. One angle of a parallelogram is 68°.
Determine the measures of the other angles.

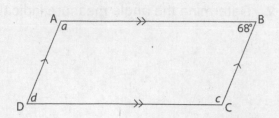

a and 68° are the measures of interior angles
between parallel sides AD and BC.

So, *a* + 68° = _____

$$a = \text{_____} - 68°$$

$$a = \text{_____}$$

a and *d* are the measures of _____ angles between parallel sides ____ and ____.
So, the relationship between *a* and *d* is: _____
Substitute: *a* = _____

d = _____

c = _____

5. Determine the angle measure indicated by the letter *s*.

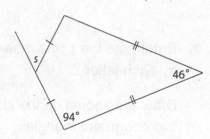

s = _____

6. The owner of a house wants to build a deck in the shape of a quadrilateral.
The deck will be built between the house and a fence, as shown below.
Determine the angle measure *m* between the deck and the fence.

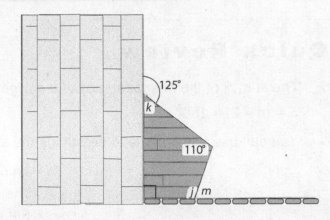

k = _____

j = _____

m = _____

7. City streets form the borders of a park.
The park has the shape of a parallelogram.
Determine the interior angles of the park.

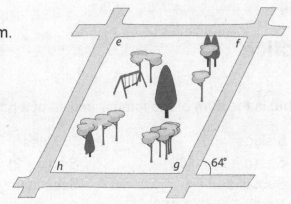

g = _____   h = _____   e = _____   f = _____

Quick Review

➤ The sum S of the interior angles of a polygon with n sides is given by the formula:

$S = (n - 2) \times 180°$

➤ You can use this formula to determine the sum of the interior angles of any polygon.

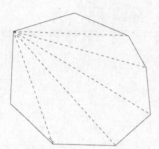

An octagon has 8 sides.
The sum of the interior angles is:
$S = (n - 2) \times 180°$
Substitute: $n = 8$
$S = (8 - 2) \times 180°$
$\quad = 6 \times 180°$
$\quad = 1080°$
The sum of the interior angles
of an octagon is 1080°.

➤ The sum of the exterior angles of any polygon is 360°.

Practice

1. What is the sum of the interior angles of a polygon with each number of sides?

a) 6 sides
$S = (n - 2) \times 180°$
Substitute: $n = $ ___
$S = ($ ___ $- 2) \times 180°$
$\quad = $ ___ $\times 180°$
$\quad = $ ____

The sum of the interior
angles of a 6-sided
polygon is _____.

b) 16 sides
$S = (n - 2) \times 180°$
Substitute: _____
$S = $ _____
$\quad = $ _____
$\quad = $ _____

The sum of the interior
angles of a 16-sided
polygon is _____.

c) 24 sides
$S = (n - 2) \times 180°$

The sum of the interior
angles of a 24-sided
polygon is _____.

2. Determine the angle measure indicated by x.

a)

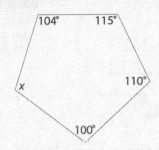

$S = (n - 2) \times 180°$

Substitute: $n = $ ____

$S = (\_\_\_ - 2) \times 180°$

$ = \_\_\_ \times 180°$

$ = \_\_\_\_\_$

The sum of the interior angles is ____.
Another way to write the sum of the interior angles is:

$x + 104° + \_\_\_\_\_ + \_\_\_\_\_ + \_\_\_\_\_$

$= x + \_\_\_\_\_$

So, $x + \_\_\_\_\_ = \_\_\_\_\_$

$ x = \_\_\_\_\_ - \_\_\_\_\_$

$ x = \_\_\_\_\_$

b)

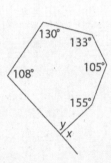

$S = (n - 2) \times 180°$

Substitute: _____

$S = _____$

$ = _____$

$ = \_\_\_\_\_$

The sum of the interior angles is ____.
Another way to write the sum of the interior angles is:

$y + \_\_\_\_\_ + \_\_\_\_\_ + \_\_\_\_\_ + \_\_\_\_\_ + \_\_\_\_\_$

$= y + \_\_\_\_\_$

So, $y + \_\_\_\_\_ = \_\_\_\_\_$

$ y = \_\_\_\_\_ - \_\_\_\_\_$

$ y = \_\_\_\_\_$

Since x and y form a straight angle,

$x + y = \_\_\_\_\_$

So, $x + \_\_\_\_ = \_\_\_\_\_$

$ x = _____$

$ x = \_\_\_\_$

73

3. A regular polygon has all sides equal and all angles equal. Determine the measure of one interior angle in a regular polygon with each number of sides.

Tip
The number of sides equals the number of angles.

a) 9 sides

$S = (n - 2) \times 180°$

Substitute: $n =$ ___

$S = (\_\_\_ - 2) \times 180°$

$= \_\_\_ \times 180°$

$= _____$

Since the angles are equal, divide by 9 to determine the measure of each angle.

$\dfrac{}{9} = \_\_\_\_\_$

Each interior angle is _____.

b) 15 sides

$S = (n - 2) \times 180°$

Substitute: _____

$S = _____$

$= _____$

$= \_\_\_\_\_$

Since the angles are equal, divide by _____ to determine the measure of each angle.

$\dfrac{}{} = \_\_\_\_\_$

Each interior angle is _____.

4. Determine the measure of one exterior angle for each regular polygon. Give your answer to 1 decimal place where necessary.

a) 8 sides

The sum of the exterior angles of any polygon is 360°.

This polygon has ___ angles.

$\dfrac{360°}{} = \_\_\_\_$

Each exterior angle is _____.

b) 13 sides

This polygon has ____ angles.

$\dfrac{}{} \doteq _____$

Each exterior angle is _____.

5. A concave polygon has an interior angle that is a reflex angle.

Tip
A reflex angle measures between 180° and 360°.

a) Measure the angles in this concave polygon. Label the diagram with the angle measures.

b) Determine the sum of the interior angles. The sum of the interior angles is _____.

c) Does the concave polygon obey this relationship: Interior angle sum = $(n - 2) \times 180°$? Justify your answer.

_____

_____

6. This picture shows the pattern of tiles on a floor.
It is made up of 3 different regular polygons.

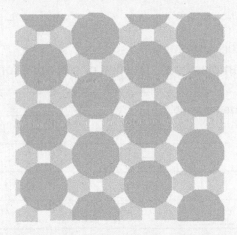

a) Determine the measure of one interior angle for each polygon.

    i) 12 sides   **ii)** 4 sides   **iii)** 6 sides

b) Determine the measure of one exterior angle for each polygon.

    i) 12 sides   **ii)** 4 sides   **iii)** 6 sides

In Your Words

Here are some of the important mathematical words of this chapter.
Build your own glossary by recording definitions and examples here. The first one is done for you.

---

interior angles (in a polygon) _angles inside_
the polygon
For example, the interior angles in this
quadrilateral are
a, b, c, and d.

---

exterior angle _____

_____

_____

_____

_____

_____

---

interior angles (in a diagram of two parallel lines intersected by a transversal) _____

_____

_____

_____

_____

_____

---

alternate angles _____

_____

_____

_____

_____

_____

---

corresponding angles _____

_____

_____

_____

_____

---

transversal _____

_____

_____

_____

_____

List other mathematical words you need to know.

_____

Chapter Review

1. Determine the measure of the unknown angle.

a)

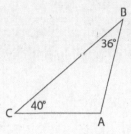

∠A = _____

b)

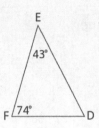

∠D = ____

2. Can a triangle have 2 interior angles that are obtuse? Justify your answer.

_____

_____

_____

3. Determine the measure of the exterior angle.

a)

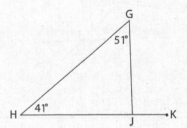

∠GJK = ____

b)

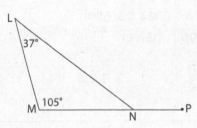

∠LNP = _____

4. A train travels in a straight line on a bridge over a river.
The river runs between 2 parallel roads.
Determine the measures of angles *s* and *t*.

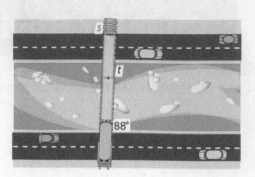

s = _____ and *t* = _____

5. Determine the unknown angles.
Label each angle relationship as corresponding, alternate, or interior.

a)

b)

c)

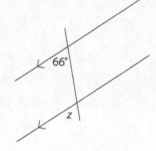

x = _____

These are _____

angles.

y = _____

These are _____

angles.

z = _____

These are _____

angles.

6. A transversal forms a 53° angle with one line
and a 137° angle with a second line as shown.
Are the two lines parallel?
Justify your answer.

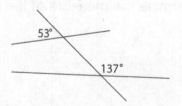

_____
_____
_____
_____

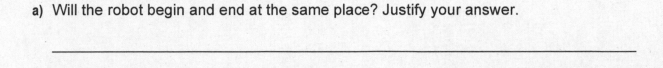

3.4 **7.** A robot is programmed to move forward 3 m and turn right 75°.
It repeats this instruction 4 times.

a) Will the robot begin and end at the same place? Justify your answer.

_____

_____

_____

b) How could you change the instructions so the path of the robot forms a quadrilateral?

_____

8. Determine the measure of the unknown angles in the parallelogram.

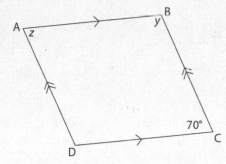

$y =$ _____ and $z =$ _____

3.5 **9.** A stop sign is a regular polygon with 8 sides.
What is the measure of each interior angle?

Each interior angle is _____.

10. Determine the angle measure indicated by *x*.

a)

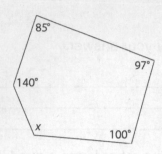

$$x = \_\_\_\_\_$$

b)

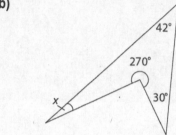

$$x = \_\_\_\_$$

11. Compare the 2 polygons.
Is the sum of the exterior angles for the hexagon greater than the sum of exterior angles for the pentagon? Justify your answer.

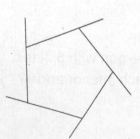 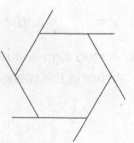

_____

_____

Proportional Reasoning

Just for Fun

Find the Rectangles

A Game for **2**

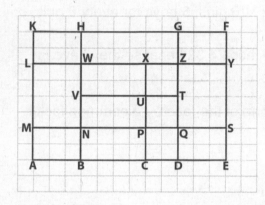

Hint

To find them all, you'll need a separate sheet of paper!

Fill in the blanks on the grid below using the diagram above. How many rectangles can you find? After you have finished, see if you can find a relationship among any of the rectangles.

Rectangle	Shortest Side	Longest Side	Shortest Side / Longest Side
KHWL	2	3	$\frac{2}{3}$
WZQN		6	$\frac{}{6}$

Quick Review

A ratio is a comparison of two quantities.
The Stars drama club has 24 boys and 32 girls.
The ratio of boys to girls is 24:32.

Equivalent ratios make the same comparison.
In The Stars drama club, there are 12 boys for every 16 girls, 6 boys for every 8 girls, or 3 boys for every 4 girls.
The ratios 12:16, 6:8, and 3:4 are equivalent to the ratio 24:32 because they have the same meaning—there are $\frac{3}{4}$ as many boys as girls.

Equivalent ratios can be formed by dividing each term of the ratio by a common factor.

$24{:}32 = \frac{24}{2} : \frac{32}{2}$

$\phantom{24{:}32} = 12{:}16$

24:32 and 12:16 are equivalent ratios.

Equivalent ratios can also be formed by multiplying each term by the same number.
$6{:}8 = (6 \times 2){:}(8 \times 2)$
$\phantom{6{:}8} = 12{:}16$

6:8 and 12:16 are equivalent ratios.

Practice

1. Determine an equivalent ratio by dividing.

   a) 10:12

   $= \frac{10}{2} : \frac{12}{}$

   $= 5{:}\underline{}$

   b) 8:18

   $= \frac{8}{} : \frac{18}{}$

   $= \underline{}$

   c) 21:14

   $= \frac{21}{7} :$

   $= \underline{}$

   d) 8:2

   $= \underline{}$

   e) 15:18

   $= \underline{}$

   f) 30:40

   $= \underline{}$

2. Determine an equivalent ratio by multiplying.

a) 10:12 = (10 × 2):(12 × __2__)
      = 20:____

b) 8:18
      8:18 = (8 × ____):(18 × ____)
           = ____:____

c) 21:14
      21:14 = (21 × ____):(14 × ____)
           = ____:____

d) 8:4

3. Determine three equivalent ratios for each ratio.

a) 30:42 = (30 × 2):(42 × 2)
           = ____:____

30:42 = $\frac{30}{}$: $\frac{42}{}$

           = ____:____

30:42 =

           = ____:____

b) 105:90 = (105 × 2):(90 × 2)
           = ____:____

105:90 =

           = ____:____

105:90 =

           = ____:____

4. Name all pairs of equivalent ratios.

5:8   12:8   9:6   4:8   5:10   15:24

> **Tip**
> *Look for ratios that have terms that are multiples of each other.*

5. For each pair of ratios, write equivalent ratios with the same first term.

a) 3:5 and 4:7
The least common multiple of 3 and 4 is 12.
3:5 = (3 × 4):(5 × ____) = 12: ____
4:7 = (4 × ____):(7 × ____) = _____

> **Hint**
> *The first term in this pair of ratios has to be a multiple of 3 and 4.*

b) 5:7 and 3:4
5:7 =
3:4 =

c) 7:3 and 5:2
7:3 =
5:2 =

6. For each pair of ratios, write equivalent ratios with the same second term.

a) 3:5 and 4:7
3:5 =
4:7 =

b) 5:4 and 7:3
5:4 =
7:3 =

7. Maria uses juice concentrate and water in the ratio 6:8.
Mark uses juice concentrate and water in the ratio 21:28.
Is the ratio of juice concentrate to water equivalent for Maria and Mark?

The least common multiple of 8 and 28 is _____.

Maria's juice	Mark's juice
$6:8 = (6 \times$ ___$):(8 \times$ ___$)$	$21:28 = (21 \times$ ___$):(28 \times$ ___$)$
= _____	= _____

> **Tip**
>
> *The amount of water is the second term of each ratio. So, write the ratios with the same second term.*

---

8. Raji mixes 3 cans of white paint with 4 cans of green paint.
Amy mixes 5 cans of white paint with 7 cans of green paint.
Who mixes the darker shade of green? Explain.

Raji's paint	Amy's paint
$3:4 =$	$5:7 =$
=	=

---

9. A ramp leading up to a concert stage is
to be built in a local park.
A scale model of the ramp is 1 cm high
and 12 cm long. The actual ramp will be 25 cm high.
What will the horizontal distance of the actual ramp be?

The horizontal distance of the actual ramp will be _____ cm.

10. The ratio of the two shorter sides of a triangle is 3:4. Using this ratio, Andy draws a larger triangle on a piece of paper. The ratio of the two shorter sides of the larger triangle is 18:25.
Did Andy draw the triangle correctly?

Quick Review

A **proportion** is a statement that two ratios are equal.
Proportions can be used to solve for unknown values.

Irene can fill 6 bags with leaves in the same time that Ron can fill 12 bags.
If Irene filled 36 bags, how many did Ron fill?

Here are two ways to determine the number of bags Ron filled.

Multiply *between* ratios.

$$\times ?$$

$$6:12 = 36:b$$

Think: What do we multiply 6 by to get 36? Multiply 12 by the same number.

$$6 \times 6 = 36$$
$$12 \times 6 = b$$
$$b = 72$$

Multiply *within* ratios.

$$\times ?$$

$$6:12 = 36:b$$

Think: What do we multiply 6 by to get 12? Multiply 36 by the same number.

$$6 \times 2 = 12$$
$$36 \times 2 = b$$
$$b = 72$$

Ron filled 72 bags.

Practice

1. Multiply between ratios to determine each value of p.

   a) $3:5 = 12:p$ Find a relationship *between* ratios.

   $3 \times \underline{\quad} = 12$

   $3:5 = (3 \times \underline{\quad}):(5 \times \underline{\quad})$ Multiply 5 by the same number.

   $= \underline{\quad}:\underline{\quad}$

   So, $p = \underline{\quad}$

   b) $4:3 = 20:p$ Find a relationship *between* ratios.

   $4 \times \underline{\quad} = \underline{\quad}$

   $4:3 = (4 \times \underline{\quad}):(3 \times \underline{\quad})$ Multiply 3 by the same number.

   $= \underline{\quad\quad}$

   So, $p = \underline{\quad}$

   c) $p:6 = 12:18$ d) $7:p = 14:12$

   $6 \times \underline{\quad} = \underline{\quad}$

   $(p \times \underline{\quad}):(\underline{\quad} \times \underline{\quad}) = 12:\underline{\quad}$

   $p \times \underline{\quad} = 12$

   So, $p = \underline{\quad}$

   e) $15:12 = p:4$ f) $p:6 = 21:18$

2. Multiply within ratios to determine each value of n.

   a) $5:15 = n:6$ b) $n:4 = 6:12$ c) $6:18 = 5:n$

   $5 \times \underline{\quad} = 15$ $6 \times \underline{\quad} = \underline{\quad}$

   $n \times \underline{\quad} = 6$ $n \times \underline{\quad} = \underline{\quad}$

   So, $n = \underline{\quad}$ So, $n = \underline{\quad}$

   d) $n:5 = 16:4$ e) $3:n = 8:24$ f) $2:8 = 16:n$

3. Kira studies for a test.

She answers 7 out of 8 practice questions correctly.

There are 120 questions on the test.

How many questions should she expect to answer correctly?

Let n be the number of questions answered correctly.

So, $7:8 = n:120$

$8 \times \underline{\quad} = 120$

$7 \times \underline{\quad} = n$

So, $n = \underline{\quad}$

Kira should expect to answer $\underline{\quad}$ questions correctly.

4. A pizza that serves 8 people calls for 2 cups of sauce and 4 cups of cheese. How much sauce and cheese are needed to make a pizza for 12 people?

Hint

It is helpful to simplify one of the ratios in a proportion.

Let n be the amount of sauce needed.

$8:2 = 12:n$

Use mental math to determine an equivalent ratio for 8:2.

Divide each term by $\underline{\quad}$.

$8:2 = \frac{8}{\quad} : \frac{2}{\quad}$

$\quad = \underline{\quad}$

$\underline{\quad} = 12:n$

$(\underline{\quad} \times \underline{\quad}):(\underline{\quad} \times \underline{\quad}) = 12:n$

So, $n = \underline{\quad}$

To make enough pizza for 12 people, $\underline{\quad}$ cups of sauce are needed.

Let c be the amount of cheese needed.

$8:4 = 12:c$

Use mental math to determine an equivalent ratio for 8:4.

Divide each term by $\underline{\quad}$.

$8:4 = \frac{8}{\quad} : \frac{4}{\quad}$

$\quad = \underline{\quad}$

$\underline{\quad} = 12:c$

$\underline{\quad\quad} = 10:c$

So, $c = \underline{\quad}$

To make enough pizza for 12 people, $\underline{\quad}$ cups of cheese are needed.

5. Douglas earned $40 working 4 h.

How much will he earn in 18 h?

Douglas will earn $\underline{\quad}$ in 18 h.

6. A hummingbird in flight beats its wings 530 times in 10 s.
How many times will it beat its wings in 1 min?

A hummingbird's wings will beat _____ times in 1 min.

7. Determine the value of each variable.

a) $14:8 = 7:y$
$14 \div \underline{\quad} = 7$
$8 \div 2 = \underline{\quad}$
So, $y = \underline{\quad}$

b) $6:33 = z:11$
$33 \div \underline{\quad} = \underline{\quad}$
$\underline{\quad} \div \underline{\quad} = z$
So, $z = \underline{\quad}$

c) $15:n = 45:18$

d) $a:5 = 12:3$
$12:3 = \frac{12}{3}:\frac{3}{3}$
So, $a:5 = \underline{\quad}:1$
$5 \div 5 = \underline{\quad}$
$a \div 5 = \underline{\quad}$
So, $a = \underline{\quad}$

e) $8:c = 12:15$
$12:15 = \frac{12}{15}:\frac{15}{15}$
So, $8:c = \underline{\quad}:\underline{\quad}$
$8 \div \underline{\quad} = \underline{\quad}$
$c \div \underline{\quad} = \underline{\quad}$
So, $c = \underline{\quad}$

f) $85:5 = 153:m$

8. To make punch for 6 people, Hessna mixed 4 cans of orange juice, 2 cans of cranberry juice, and 6 cans of water.
How much of each would she need to make punch for 15 people?

Orange juice: Cranberry juice: Water:

> **Tip**
> *Calculate each ratio separately.*

Hessna would need ___ cans of orange juice, ___ cans of cranberry juice, and ___ cans of water.

Quick Review

When you compare two quantities with different units, you have a rate.
For example, kilometres and hours.

If you want to compare two rates, you first have to calculate the unit rate.
For example, kilometres per hour (or how many kilometres can be driven in 1 h).

Suppose Maria earned $37.80 working 4 h and Josh earned $63.70 working 7 h.
Who has the better-paying job?

Compare the unit pay rates for Maria and Josh.

In 4 h, Maria earned $37.80.
So, in 1 h, she earned $37.80 ÷ 4 = $9.45.

In 7 h, Josh earned $63.70.
So, in 1 h, he earned $63.70 ÷ 7 = $9.10.

Maria's hourly rate is higher.

If Maria and Josh worked the same number of hours, Maria would be paid more.
So, Maria has the better-paying job.

Practice

1. Determine each unit rate.

a) 5 kg of strawberries for $21.40

$$\frac{21.40}{5} = \underline{\hspace{2cm}}$$

The unit rate is _____.

b) 1260 km flown in 4 h

$$\underline{\hspace{1cm}} = \underline{\hspace{2cm}}$$

The unit rate is _____.

c) $65.80 earned in 7 h

The unit rate is _____.

d) 522 words typed in 9 min

The unit rate is _____.

2. Approximately 1 369 000 cars are produced in Canada in 1 year.
What is the average number of cars produced per day?

1 369 000 cars per year

1 369 000 cars in _____ days

$\dfrac{1\,369\,000}{}$ cars per day

So, an average of _____ cars are produced per day.

3. A 700-g box of Oat Zeros cereal costs $3.15.
A 1.35-kg box of Captain Blue cereal costs $6.48.
Which is the better buy? Explain.

a) 700 g is 7 × 100 g; so, the cost of 100 g of Oat Zeros is: $\dfrac{\$3.15}{7} =$ _____

b) 1.35 kg = _____ g

_____ g is _____ × 100 g; so, the cost of 100 g of Captain Blue is: $\dfrac{}{} =$ _____

_____

4. Sara wants to redo the floor in her apartment.
She compared the cost of floor tiles to the cost of carpet.
22 m^2 of floor tiles costs $1133.00.
94 m^2 of carpet costs $4535.50.
Which floor covering is more expensive per square metre?

Unit cost of the floor tiles:

Unit cost of the carpet:

_____

_____

5. Kurtis typed 720 words in 16 min. Tara typed 560 words in 14 min.
Who typed faster?

Kurtis: Tara:

_____

6. A 310-g jar of peanut butter costs $2.79.
   A 1-kg jar of the same brand of peanut butter costs $8.60.
   Which is the better buy?

◀ ·········· Hint

Find the cost of 100 g of each.

_____

7. Which carton of juice is the best buy: A 1-L carton of juice for $1.58, a 1.89-L carton of the same juice for $3.10, or a 2.84-L carton of the same juice for $4.54?

_____

8. Store A charges $7.80 per storage box.
   For a limited time, Store A has a sale offering "Buy 2 get 1 Free".
   Store B sells the same storage boxes at a cost of $5.70 each.
   Jacquie wants to buy 4 boxes. From which store should she buy?

   At Store A, Jacqui pays for 3 boxes.
   $3 \times \$7.80 =$ _____
   At Store B, Jacqui pays for 4 boxes.
   ___ $\times \$5.70 =$ _____
   She should buy from Store ___.

> **Tip**
> *Another way to think about Store A's sale is that for every 3 boxes, you only pay for 2.*

Quick Review

A car travels 100 km on 8 L of gasoline.
How far will the car travel on 50 L of gasoline?

Use proportional reasoning to calculate the distance for each volume of gasoline.

The car uses 8 L of gasoline to travel 100 km.

So, the car uses 1 L of gasoline to travel: $\frac{100}{8}$ km = 12.5 km

Then, the car will travel: $12.5 \times 50 = 62.5$ km on 50 L of gasoline.

How much gasoline is needed to travel 2500 km?

The car travels 100 km on 8 L of gasoline.

So, the car travels 1 km on $\frac{8}{100}$ L = 0.08 L of gasoline.

$0.08 \times 2500 = 200$ L

The car needs 200 L of gasoline to travel 2500 km.

Practice

1. A machine prints 72 labels in 3 min.

   a) How many labels does the machine print in 1 min?
      The machine prints 72 labels in 3 min.

      The machine prints $\frac{72}{3}$ = _____ labels in 1 min.

      The machine prints _____ labels/min.

   b) How long will it take the machine to print 480 labels?
      The machine prints _____ labels in 1 min.

      Printing 480 labels will take $\frac{480}{}$ = _____ min.

      The machine takes _____ min to print 480 labels.

c) In seconds, how long does it take to print 1 label?

◀ ········· **Hint**

Hint
Think about how many labels the machine can print in 1 min. Then, convert minutes to seconds.

There are _____ s in 1 min.
The machine prints _____ labels in 1 min.

It takes _____ s to print 1 label.

d) The machine breaks down after 35 min. How many labels were printed?

Tip
Multiply to see if your answer is reasonable.

_____ labels were printed in 35 min.

2. Ribbon costs $2.88 for 4 m.

a) How much does 1 m of ribbon cost?

b) How much does 12.5 m of ribbon cost?

1 m of ribbon costs _____.

12.5 m of ribbon costs _____.

c) How much ribbon can be bought for $3.60?

$3.60 can buy _____ of ribbon.

3. Charles is planning to visit England.
He can exchange $21 Canadian for £10 (10 British pounds).

a) How many British pounds will Charles get for $400 Canadian?
$21 can be exchanged for £10.

$1 can be exchanged for $\frac{£10}{21}$ = £_____.

$400 can be exchanged for £_____ × 400 = £_____.

b) How many Canadian dollars will he get for £25?
£10 can be exchanged for $21.

£1 can be exchanged for $\frac{\$21}{10}$ = $_____.

£25 can be exchanged for $_____ × 25 = $_____.

4. Karl is in Europe visiting relatives.
He can exchange $14 Canadian for 10 Euros.

a) How many Euros would Karl get for $350 Canadian?

b) When Karl returns to Canada, he has 45 Euros.
What is that amount in Canadian dollars?

5. A car travelled 98 km on 7 L of gasoline.

Tip
If you need help,
use the example in
the Quick Review at
the beginning of this
lesson.

a) How far will the car travel on
30 L of gasoline?

b) How much gasoline is needed
to travel 350 km?

Then, the car uses 30 L of
gasoline to travel: ___ × ___ = _____.

The car needs _____ of gasoline
to travel 350 km.

6. Harold earned $55.50 working 6 h.

a) How much will Harold earn
if he works 20 h?

b) How long will it take Harold to earn $740?

It will take Harold _____ to earn $740.

7. The actual distance between 2 towns is 620 km.
On a map, this distance is 12.4 cm.
On the same map, the distance between 2 other towns is 9.3 cm.
What is the actual distance between these 2 towns?

Quick Review

An unknown value in a proportion can be found using algebra.
Jason earned $72 working 6 h.
How much would he earn working 18 h?

Solve a proportion using *within* ratios.

$72... in... 6 h

n dollars... in... 18 h

$72:6 = n:18$

$$\frac{72}{6} = \frac{n}{18}$$

To isolate n, multiply each side of the equation by 18.

$$18 \times \frac{72}{6} = \frac{n}{18} \times 18$$

$$\frac{1296}{6} = n$$

$$n = 216$$

Solve a proportion using *between* ratios.

$72... in... 6 h

n dollars... in... 18 h

$$\frac{n}{72} = \frac{18}{6}$$

To isolate n, multiply each side of the equation by 72.

$$72 \times \frac{n}{72} = \frac{18}{6} \times 72$$

$$n = \frac{1296}{6}$$

$$n = 216$$

Practice

1. Solve for p.

   a) $\dfrac{p}{8} = \dfrac{3}{4}$

   ____ $\times \dfrac{p}{8} = \dfrac{3}{4} \times$ ____

   $p =$ ____

   b) $\dfrac{p}{7} = \dfrac{6}{21}$

   ____ $\times \dfrac{p}{7} =$ ____ $\times$ ____

   $p =$ ____

   c) $\dfrac{p}{15} = \dfrac{7}{3}$

   d) $\dfrac{p}{12} = \dfrac{7}{3}$

2. Solve for each variable.

   a) $n{:}3 = 24{:}8$

   __ $= \dfrac{24}{}$

   ____ $\times \dfrac{n}{3} = \dfrac{24}{} \times 3$

   $n =$ ___

   b) $z{:}28 = 3{:}84$

   __ $=$ __

   ____ $\times$ __ $=$ __ $\times$ ____

   $z =$ ___

   c) $a{:}49 = 4{:}7$

   d) $y{:}128 = 1{:}16$

3. A computer-repair company charges $310 for 2.5 h of work.
   How much would the computer-repair company charge for 8 h of work?

   Let z dollars represent the amount the company will charge.

   The computer-repair company would charge _____ for 8 h of work.

4. A man working on a film set is 1.8 m tall. He is building a miniature set for filming.
The man's version of himself in the miniature set is 3 cm tall.

A flagpole on location is 12 m tall.
How tall will the pole be in the miniature set?

◄ ·········· Hint

Remember metric
conversions:
1 m = 100 cm

Let h be the height of the flagpole in the miniature.
Convert metres to centimetres.
The man's height in centimetres is: 1 8 × _____ = _____
The flagpole's height in centimetres is: 12 × _____ = _____

The ratio of the miniature flagpole's height to the real flagpole's height is h:_____.
The ratio of the man's height in the miniature to the real man's height is 3:_____.

So, h:_____ = 3:_____.

Write each ratio in fraction form.

To isolate h, multiply each side of the equation by _____.
h = ____
The miniature flagpole will be _____ high.

5. A website gets 1110 hits in 5 h.
At that rate, how many hits would the website get over 24 h?

Tip
First, decide what
variable to use.
Then, write a ratio.

The website would get _____ hits over 24 h.

6. A museum is open 8 h a day. The museum gets about 136 visitors a day.
For special events, the museum is open for 14 h.
If the visitors continue at the same rate, how many visitors should the museum expect on
the day of a special event?

The museum should expect _____ visitors on the day of a special event.

7. A rectangle has a length-to-width ratio of 8:5.

What is the measure of the unknown side in the following rectangles if the length-to-width ratio is the same?

a) Length = 24 cm

Let q represent the unknown width.

$$\frac{q}{24} = \frac{5}{8}$$

$$\underline{\hspace{1cm}} \times \frac{q}{24} = \frac{5}{8} \times \underline{\hspace{1cm}}$$

$q = \underline{\hspace{1cm}}$

Width = $\underline{\hspace{2cm}}$

b) Width = 65 cm

Let p represent the unknown length.

$$\frac{p}{65} = \underline{\hspace{0.5cm}}$$

$$\underline{\hspace{1cm}} \times \frac{p}{65} = \underline{\hspace{0.5cm}} \times \underline{\hspace{1cm}}$$

$p = \underline{\hspace{1cm}}$

Length = $\underline{\hspace{2cm}}$

c) Width = 80 cm

d) Length = 80 cm

8. A statue is 2.8 m tall. It casts a shadow 1.2 m long.

A flag beside the statue casts a shadow 2.1 m long. How high is the flag?

9. Jenna can sell 35 boxes of cookies in 2 h.

If she needs to sell 280 boxes, how many hours must she work?

Quick Review

A **percent** is a ratio that compares a number to 100.
For example, 45% is the same as 45:100.
A percent can also be expressed as a fraction or a decimal.

$$45\% = \frac{45}{100} = 0.45$$

A mountain bike that regularly sells for $240 is on sale for 20% off.
The sale price is 100% − 20% = 80% of the original price.

Let p dollars represent the sale price of the bike.

p:240 = 80:100

$$\frac{p}{240} = \frac{80}{100}$$

To isolate p, multiply each side of the equation by 240.

$$240 \times \frac{p}{240} = \frac{80}{100} \times 240$$

$$p = 192$$

The sale price is $192.

Consumers in Ontario have to pay 14% tax on purchases.
The total price is 100% + 14% = 114% of the sale price.

Let t represent the total price including tax on a purchase of $192.

$$\frac{t}{192} = \frac{114}{100}$$

Multiply each side of the equation by 192.

$$192 \times \frac{t}{192} = \frac{114}{100} \times 192$$

$$t = 218.88$$

Tip
114% of 192 is
1.14 × 192 = 218.88.

The total price is $218.88.

Practice

1. Write each percent as a fraction and as a decimal.

   a) 27%

   $\frac{27}{100}$, _____

   b) 39%

   $\frac{}{100}$, 0.39

   c) 50%

   _____, _____

   d) 25%

   e) 12%

   f) 112%

2. Write each fraction as a decimal and as a percent.

   a) $\frac{63}{100}$

   0.63, _____%

   b) $\frac{29}{100}$

   _____, 29%

   c) $\frac{71}{100}$

   _____, _____%

   d) $\frac{9}{50}$

   e) $\frac{7}{25}$

   f) $\frac{41}{25}$

3. Determine each value.

   a) 15% of $20

   15% = _____

   0.15 × $20 = _____

   b) 40% of 135 g

   40% = _____

   _____ × 135 g = _____

   c) 150% of 90 m

   150% = _____

   _____ × _____ = _____

   d) 5% of $6800

   e) 110% of 650 kg

   f) 83% of 200 L

4. In a survey of 240 students, 45% said they regularly participate in outdoor sports. Of the students who participated in the survey, how many regularly participate in outdoor sports?

   Of the students who participated in the survey, _____ regularly participate in outdoor sports.

5. A flat panel TV is on sale for $1100. Taxes are 14%.

   a) How much is the tax on the TV?

Tip
Refer to the Quick Review at the beginning of this lesson if you need help.

b) What is the price of the TV including taxes?

_____

6. Charlie borrows $580 for 9 months.
   The annual interest rate is 8%.
   How much simple interest does Charlie pay?

   $I = Prt$
   I is the simple interest in dollars.
   The principal, P, is $_____.
   The annual interest rate, r, is ___ % or _____.

   The time, t, as a fraction of a year is $\dfrac{}{12}$.

   So, $I =$ _____ $\times$ _____ $\times \dfrac{}{12}$

   $=$ _____

   Charlie pays _____ simple interest.

7. Jodi puts $360 into a savings account for 7 months.
   The annual interest rate is 3%.

   a) How much simple interest did she earn in 7 months?

_____

   b) How much money is in her account at the end of 7 months?

_____

In Your Words

Here are some of the important mathematical words of this unit.
Build your own glossary by recording definitions and examples here. The first one is done for you.

ratio <u>a comparison of two quantities</u> <u>For example, if there is 1 teacher for</u> <u>every 8 students, the ratio of teachers to</u> <u>students is 1:8.</u>	**rate**
equivalent ratios	**unit rate**
proportional	**percent**

List other mathematical words you need to know.

_____

Chapter Review

LESSON
4.1 **1.** Determine 2 equivalent ratios for each ratio.

    a) 3:7   **b)** 6:15

2. On a ski trip, 4 out of every 7 males want to
snowboard and 3 out of every 5 females
want to snowboard.
There are an equal number of males and
females on the trip.

Do more males than females want to snowboard? ◄ ··············

> **Hint**
>
> *Compare the rates by
> finding an equal second
> term.*

4.2 **3.** Determine each value of n.

    a) n:10 = 3:5   **b)** 7:4 = 21:n **c)** 6:n = 2:5

4. The ratio of rolled oats to flour in a recipe for muffins is 7:6.
If Russ has 350 g of rolled oats, how much flour will he need?

---

5. Determine each unit rate.

    a) $73.50 earned in 6 h   **b)** $4.44 for 12 cans of pop

    c) 128 km cycled in 8 h   **d)** 56 points scored in 7 games

6. At Food Palace, 3 cases of juice are on sale for $10.20.
At Grocery Tiger, 4 cases of the same juice are on sale for $13.80.
Which is the better buy?

_____

_____

7. Heather bought 3 cases of juice for $15.60.

    a) How much would it cost to buy 8 cases of juice?

_____

    b) How many cases of juice could she buy for $37?

_____

8. On a blueprint for a house, the master bedroom measures 9.6 cm by 7.2 cm. The actual room measures 4.8 m by 3.6 m.

What are the dimensions of the living room on the blueprint if the actual dimensions of the living room are 7.8 m by 3.6 m?

4.5 **9.** Solve for each missing value.

a) $\dfrac{x}{9} = \dfrac{8}{18}$

b) $\dfrac{12}{15} = \dfrac{7}{35}$

c) $\dfrac{p}{18} = \dfrac{7}{9}$

d) h:10 = 15:25

e) y:4 = 15:6

f) n:12 = 5:6

10. An 84-m^2 condominium in a new apartment block sells for \$235 000.

If the cost per square foot is the same throughout the building, what is the price of a 140-m^2 apartment? Round the answer to the nearest thousand.

Hint

Find the unit cost per square metre. Then, multiply by the area.

11. Determine each value.

a) 60% of 140 m

b) 80% of $25

c) 125% of 40 kg

d) 140% of 275 g

e) 1.5% of $800

f) 33.3% of 75 L

12. A $2500 laptop computer is on sale for 15% off the marked price.
Taxes are 14%.

a) Calculate the sale price of the computer.

_____

b) Calculate the price of the computer including taxes.

_____

13. Patrick borrowed $600 for 8 months.
The annual interest rate is 21%.

a) How much interest will Patrick owe at the end of the 8 months?

_____

b) How much will he have to pay back at the end of 8 months?

_____

Just for Fun

Word Find

Find the following words in the puzzle.

CALCULATOR   INTERVAL   DATA   GRAPH
PLOT   RELATION   SCATTER   TREND

Words may be horizontal, vertical, or diagonal. Some may be backward. A letter may be used for more than one word.

```
A E N S C A T T R E C C
H N K O I N T E R V A L
R P D P I N D A F L T K
D A A U T T P I C N A L
A G P R U O A U I L D A
T V E H G E L L P O L V
P N O T R A J W E K O E
D Y A U T W B Z R F T
J D L O S C A T T E R N
H C R A K N R T O L P I
```

Number Square

Complete the number square using numbers from 0 to 9.
The numbers in each row have the sums at the right.
The numbers in each column have the sums along the bottom.

		9		30
0		8	5	13
9			6	18
8	9		6	30
	16	26	24	

Quick Review

A scatter plot relates two different measures.

The points in this scatter plot show a relationship between the distance a car travelled and the length of time it travelled.

To determine the distance travelled after 3 h, begin at 3 on the *Time* axis.
Locate the data point above 3.
Move horizontally from the data point above 3 to the *Distance* axis.
The distance travelled was about 110 km in 3 h.

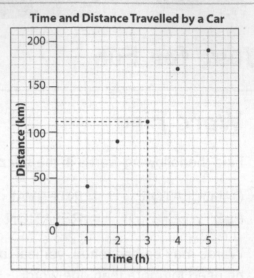

Time and Distance Travelled by a Car

A trend in the data points shows a relationship between the measures.
The points in this scatter plot show a relationship.
As you move to the right, the points go up. There is an upward trend.
As time increases, the distance travelled increases.

A scatter plot has a downward trend if the points go down as you move to the right.
If there is no trend in the data, then the points do not show a relationship.

Practice

1. Describe any trends in the data.

a)

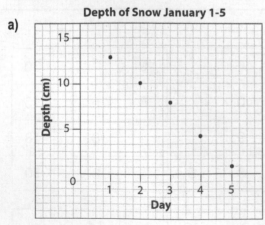

Depth of Snow January 1-5

b)

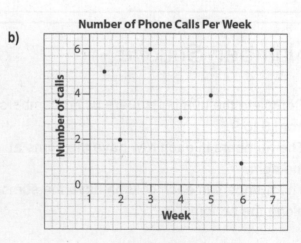

Number of Phone Calls Per Week

There is _____ (an upward trend, a downward trend, no trend) in the data. As you move to the right, the points go _____ (down, up).

There is _____ (an upward trend, a downward trend, no trend) in the data.

2. a) What does this scatter plot show?

_____
_____
_____
_____
_____
_____
_____
_____

Yellowstone Bison Population

b) What year was the population of bison about 1000: 1904, 1917, or 1927? How do you know?

_____
_____

c) What was the approximate population of bison in 1920: 250, 725, or 500?

Hint

You can draw lines on the graph to help you find the answer.

_____
_____

d) In what year did the population of bison reach about 1100?

_____

e) What was the approximate population of bison in 1922?

_____

f) There is _____ (an upward, a downward, no) trend in the data. As the years _____ (increase, decrease), the population of bison _____ (increases, decreases).

3. a) What does this scatter plot show?

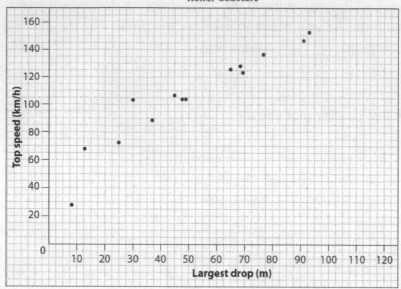

Roller Coasters

_____
_____

b) What is the approximate top speed for a
   roller coaster shown on the graph?
   How do you know?

   _____
   _____

Hint

What does the highest point on the graph represent?

c) How far must a roller coaster drop to reach a top speed of about 64 km/h. Justify your
   answer.

   _____
   _____

d) If a roller coaster reaches a top speed of 129 km/h, what is its largest drop?

   _____

e) If a roller coaster's largest drop is 46 m, what is its top speed?

   _____

f) There is an upward trend in the data.
   As the top speed of a roller coaster increases, the size of the largest drop decreases.
   Is this correct? Justify your answer.

   _____

Quick Review

Data in a scatter plot sometimes shows a trend.

South Bend High School held a series of movie nights.
The student council sold popcorn and drinks during
the events.

The scatter plot relates the number of bags of
popcorn drinks sold.
The data shows an upward trend. As the number of
bags of popcorn sold increases, the number of drinks
sold increases.

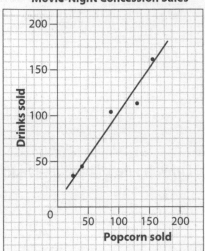

Movie-Night Concession Sales

You can draw a **line of best** fit that follows
the path of the data points.

Hint

*There should be about
as many points above
the line as below.*

Suppose the student council predicts it will
sell 175 bags of popcorn.
You can use the line of best fit to estimate the
number of drinks that will be sold.

Begin at 175 on the *Popcorn sold* axis.
Move up to the line of best fit, then over to the *Drinks sold* axis.
When 175 bags of popcorn are sold, about 190 drinks are sold.

Practice

1. Which line would you use as a line
    of best fit? Why? Justify your choice.

    _____

    _____

    _____

    _____

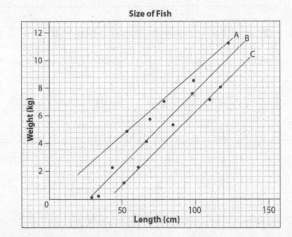

Size of Fish

2. The scatter plot shows the number of alternative fuel vehicles in the Government of Canada's on-road fleet between 1998 and 2001.

a) The data has _____ (an upward, a downward, no) trend. The number of alternative-fuel vehicles _____ (increases, decreases) as the years _____ (increase, decrease).

Alternative-Fuel Vehicles

b) Draw a line of best fit. Describe how you drew it.

_____

_____

_____

_____

_____

c) In 1995, there were about _____ (220 000, 330 000, 440 000) alternative-fuel vehicles in use.

d) In _____ (1990, 1995, 1999) there were about 420 000 alternative-fuel vehicles in use.

Hint

Begin at the year 1995 on the Year axis. Move up to the line of best fit. Then move over to the Number of vehicles axis.

e) About how many alternative-fuel vehicles were in use in 1994?

_____

f) In what year were there about 250 000 alternative-fuel vehicles in use?

_____

3. Diana works as a server in a local restaurant.

The amount she earns in tips is related to the amount of her total sales for the restaurant.

Total Sales ($)	200	320	285	420	485	255	360
Tips ($)	25	32	30	40	53	23	43

a) Plot the data on the scatter plot.

Some of the points have been plotted for you

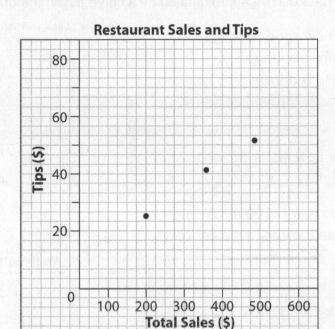

Restaurant Sales and Tips

b) What trend do you see in the data? Describe the trend.

_____

_____

c) Draw a line of best fit.

d) When Diana's total sales reach $450, how much will she receive in tips?

_____

e) If Diana earns $60 in tips, what is her total sales?

_____

> **Tip**
> *Extend the line of best fit to the right.*

Quick Review

Sometimes points on a scatter plot are related but do not lie on a straight line.
When this happens, the data can be approximated by a curve called the **curve of best fit**.

The scatter plot shows how speed and skid
length are related in traffic accidents.
A smooth curve of best fit is drawn.
The curve of best fit passes through as many
points as possible.

The police can estimate how fast a car was
travelling using skid length.

Suppose a car left a skid mark of 60 m. We can
use the curve to estimate the speed the car was
travelling.

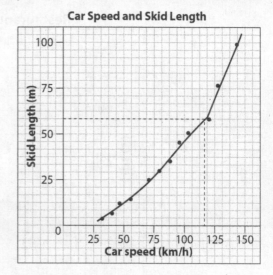
Car Speed and Skid Length

Begin at 60 m on the *Skid length* axis.
Move across to the curve, then down to the *Speed* axis.
The speed of the car was about 119 km/h.

Practice

1. Which line would you use as the curve of best fit?
Justify your answer.

_____

_____

_____

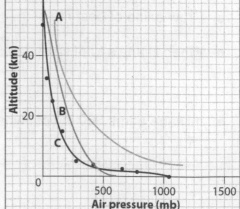
Air Pressure and Altitude

2. The scatter plot relates the age of a child with the number of hours of sleep needed per day.

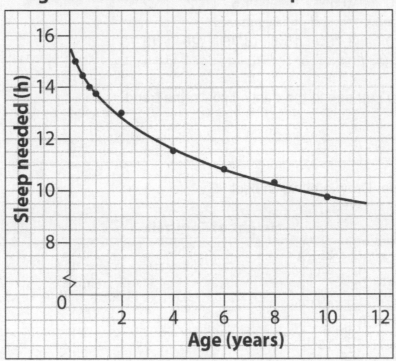

Age of Child and Hours of Sleep Needed

a) As a child's age _____ (increases, decreases), the amount of sleep needed _____ (increases, decreases).

b) Draw a curve of best fit.

Hint

Connect the points with a smooth curve. Continue the curve past the lowest point.

c) At age 2, a child should get about _____ (6 h, 13 h, 15 h) of sleep per day.

d) A child who needs approximately 11 h of sleep per day is about ____ (2, 5, 9) years old.

e) At what age do children need less than 10 h of sleep per day?

_____

f) A 3-year-old child needs approximately how much sleep per day?

_____

3. A football is kicked into the air.

The table shows the height of the football every half-second.

Time (s)	0	0.5	1	1.5	2	2.5
Height (m)	0	8.75	15	18.75	20	18.75

a) What trend do you see in the data? Explain the trend.

_____

_____

b) Graph the data. Draw a curve of best fit.

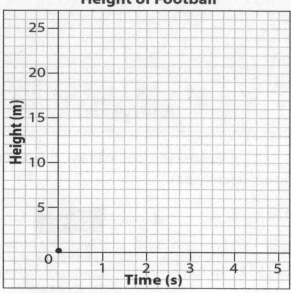

Height of Football

c) What is the football's height at 1.5 s?

_____

d) When is the football at its greatest height?

_____

d) When is the football 15 m high?

Hint

Extend the graph to the right that "mirrors" the curve.

_____

e) What does it mean when the height is 0 m?

_____

Quick Review

When a graph is a straight line, we say there is a **linear relation** between the measures shown on the graph.

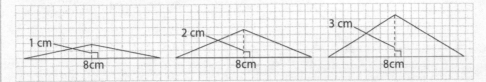

$$A = \frac{1}{2} \times 8 \times 1$$
$$= 4$$

$$A = \frac{1}{2} \times 8 \times 2$$
$$= 8$$

$$A = \frac{1}{2} \times 8 \times 3$$
$$= 12$$

Height (cm)	Area (cm²)
1	4
2	8
3	12

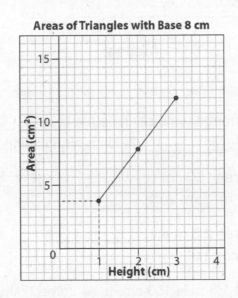

Areas of Triangles with Base 8 cm

As the height increases by 1 cm, the area increases by 4 cm².

The points on the graph lie on a straight line.
There is a linear relation between the height and area.

We can use the graph to estimate the area of a triangle with base 8 cm and height 1.5 cm. Begin at 1.5 cm on the *Height* axis. Move up to the line, then across to the *Area* axis.

The area is about 6 cm².

Practice

1. This graph shows how metres and centimetres are related.

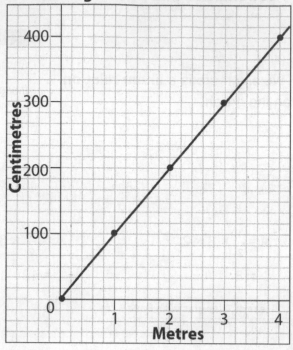

Relating Metres and Centimetres

a) The relation between metres and centimetres is _____ (linear, non-linear) because the points _____ (lie on a straight line, do not lie on a straight line).

b) An object that measures 100 cm wide is _____ (1 m, 2 m, 3 m) wide.

 Hint

Use the graph to estimate.

c) An object that measures 2.5 m tall is _____ (10 cm, 200 cm, 250 cm) tall.

c) Robbie estimates that 1.5 m is 150 cm. Is he correct? Justify your answer.

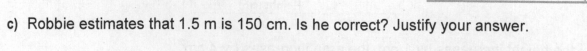

_____

e) Use the graph to estimate 7 m in centimetres.

_____

f) Use the graph to estimate 50 cm in metres.

_____

2. The student council did a penny drive to raise money.
The students put the donated pennies in a straight line.
The students determined that a line of 100 pennies, or $1 in pennies, has length 1.9 m.

a) Complete the table for the lengths
of lines of pennies from $10 to $50.

Amount ($)	Length (m)
1	1.9
10	
20	
30	
40	76
50	

> **Tip**
>
> *Multiply the dollar amount in each row by 1.9 to find the length.*

b) Graph the data. Draw a line of best fit.

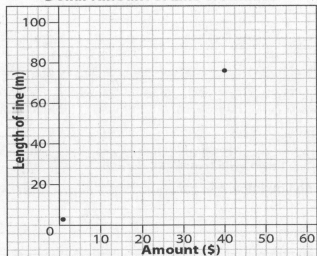

Dollar Amount of Line of Pennies

c) The relation between amount in dollars and length in metres is _____ (linear, non-linear) because the points _____ (lie on a straight line, do not lie on a straight line).

d) 12 m of pennies is about _____ ($2, $6, $10).

e) $19 in pennies has length about _____ (23 m, 30 m, 36 m).

f) Darshan donated $12.
Use the graph to estimate the length of a line of $12 in pennies.

3. George is spreading grass seed on his lawn.
The package shows 1 kg of seed covers 184 m² of lawn.

a) Complete the table of values.

Grass seed (kg)	Lawn area (m²)
1	184
2	
3	
4	
5	
6	

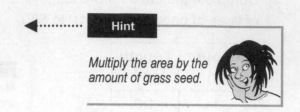

Hint

Multiply the area by the amount of grass seed.

b) Graph the data. Draw a line of best fit through the points.

Grass Seed and Lawn Area

Grass seed (kg) — vertical axis: 200, 400, 600, 800, 1000, 1200

Lawn area (cm²) — horizontal axis: 1, 2, 3, 4, 5, 6

c) Is the relationship linear? How do you know?

_____

_____

d) How much lawn could 4.5 kg of grass seed cover?

_____

e) How much grass seed would it take to cover 645 m² of lawn?

_____

f) George's neighbour uses about 5.5 kg of grass seed to cover her lawn. Use the graph to estimate the size of the lawn.

_____

Quick Review

A new computer is purchased for $1500.
Some people believe a computer's value decreases by 20% of the previous year's price every year.
The table and graph show the estimated value of the computer over time.

Time (year)	Value of computer ($)
0	1500.00
1	1200.00
2	960.00
3	768.00
4	614.40
5	491.52
6	393.22
7	314.57

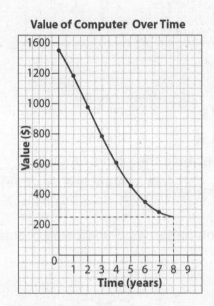

Value of Computer Over Time

The table shows that the value of the computer decreases over time.
The points of the graph lie on a curve. So, the relationship is **non-linear**.

Use the graph to estimate the value of the computer after 8 years.
Begin at 8 years on the *Time* axis.
Move up to the curve, then across to the *Value* axis.

The value of the computer after 8 years is about $250.

Practice

1. Two graphs are shown. Is each relationship linear or non-linear?

a)

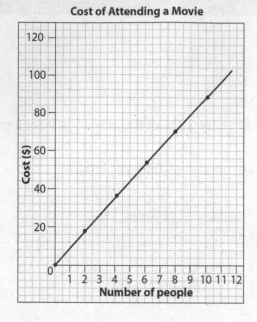

b)

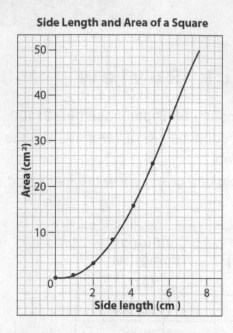

Graph A is _____ (linear, non-linear) because the points lie on ___ _____ (a straight line, a curve).

Graph B is _____ (linear, non-linear) because the points lie on _____ (a straight line, a curve).

2. The following pattern is made using circular disks.

Frame 1

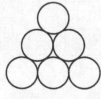

Frame 2

Frame 3

a) Draw the next 4 frames in the pattern.

b) Complete the table of values. Count the number of disks in each frame to complete the table. Graph the data.

Frame number	Number of disks
1	
2	
3	
4	
5	
6	21
7	

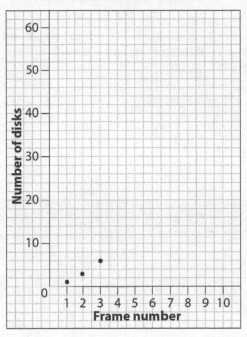

Frame and Number of Disks

c) The graph is a _____ (straight line, curve) that goes _____ (up, down) to the _____ (left, right). As the frame number _____ (increases, decreases) by _____ (1, 3, 5), the number of disks _____ (increases, decreases) by a _____ (lesser, greater) amount each time.

d) Is the rule "add the frame number to the number of disks in the previous frame" useful? How do you know?

_____

_____

e) How many disks are needed for frame number 8: 13, 36, or 59? _____

f) In what frame would you find 55 disks: 3, 7, or 10? _____

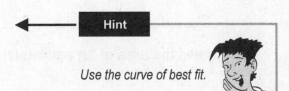

Hint

Use the curve of best fit.

g) Estimate the number of disks in frame number 9.

There will be _____ disks in frame 9.

3. The side lengths and areas of equilateral triangles are shown in the table.

a) Graph the data. Draw a curve of best fit through the points.

Side length (cm)	Area (cm²)
3	3.9
5	10.8
7	21.2
9	35.1
11	52.4

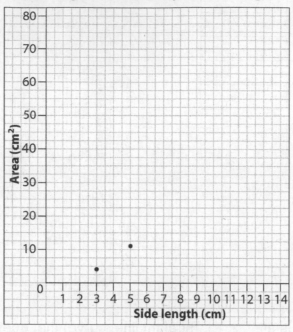

Side Length and Area of Equilateral Triangle

b) Describe the graph. What trends do you see in the data?

_____

_____

c) Is the relationship linear or non-linear? How do you know?

_____

> **Tip**
>
> *When the graph of a relationship is a curve, the relationship is non-linear.*

d) What is the area of an equilateral triangle with side length 4 cm?

_____

e) What is the side length of an equilateral triangle with area 60 cm²?

_____

Quick Review

The title of the graph and the labels on the vertical and horizontal axis tell what the graph shows.
The shape of the graph also gives information.

The graph shows Chad's distance from home as he goes on a walk.
Key points where the graph changes are labelled.

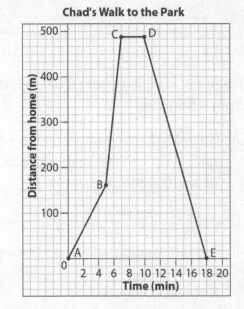

Chad's Walk to the Park

Describe Chad's walk.

At point A, Chad is at home.

From A to B, Chad walks away from home.
The graph goes up to the right.
Chad is walking for 5 min. He walks 160 m.

From B to C, Chad is still walking away from home.
The segment from B to C is steeper than the segment from A to B.
So, Chad's average speed has increased and he is walking faster.
He walks for 4 min and travels 320 m.

From C to D, the segment is horizontal.
This means that time is passing, but Chad's distance from home does not change.
Chad is standing still for 1 min.

From D to E, the segment goes down to the right.
Chad is walking toward home.
He walks 480 m in 8 min.

At point E, Chad is back at home.

Chad walked 960 m in 18 min.

Practice

1. Which graph best represents each situation?

   a) The height of a cake during a 30-minute baking process. _____

   b) The height of a grasshopper's jump. _____

   c) The height of an ice cube sitting in the sun. _____

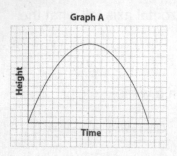

Graph A

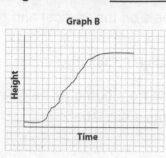

Graph B

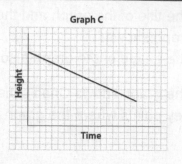

Graph C

2. Renee and Julie used a CBR motion detector to investigate changes in their distance from a flagpole.

   a) The information shown on the horizontal axis is
   the _____ (time in seconds,
   distance in metres).

   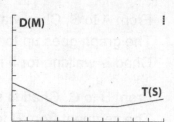

   b) The information shown on the vertical axis is
   the _____ (time in seconds,
   distance in metres).

   c) Describe the motion of the graph.

   > **Tip**
   > Read the example
   > in the quick review
   > if you need help.

   The first segment goes _____ (down to the
   right, up to the left). The distance from the flagpole is
   _____ (increasing, decreasing) at a constant speed for _____ (1 s, 3 s, 5 s).
   The second segment is _____ (vertical, horizontal). The distance _____
   _____ (increases, decreases, does not change) for _____ (1 s, 4 s, 7 s). The
   third segment goes _____ (up to the right, down to the left). The distance
   from the flagpole is _____ (increasing, decreasing).

3. Emil estimated the height of a helium-filled balloon every 2 min.
He drew this graph.

Height of Helium Balloon

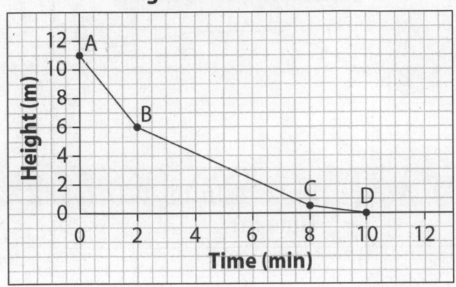

a) From A to B, the balloon's height _____ (increases, decreases) from _____ (6 m, 8 m, 11 m) to _____ (6 m, 8 m, 11 m) in _____ (2 min, 4 min, 6 min).

b) From B to C, the balloon's height _____ (increases, decreases) from _____ (6 m, 8 m, 10 m) to _____ (0.5 m, 2 m, 3.5 m) in _____ (2 min, 6 min, 8 min).

c) At point D, the balloon's height is _____ (0 m, 1 m, 2 m). Describe what this means.

_____

d) The balloon's height changed _____ (2 m, 5 m, 8 m) from A to B, _____ (1 m, 5.5 m, 10 m) from B to C, and _____ (0.5 m, 2 m, 3.5 m) from C to D.

e) It takes the balloon _____ (5 min, 10 min, 15 min) to decrease _____ (5 m, 11 m, 12 m).

f) In which segment did the balloon change in height the fastest?
Justify your answer.

_____

_____

4. The graph shows the temperature in Windsor, Ontario, during a day in June.

Temperature in Windsor, Ontario

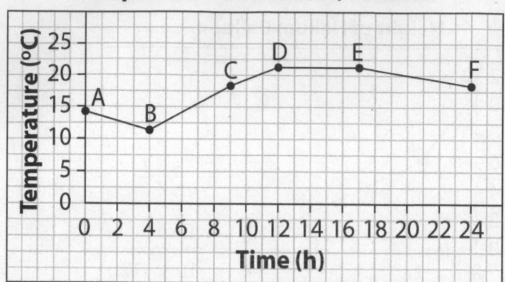

a) From A to B, the temperature _____ (increased, decreased) from _____ (12°C, 13°C, 14°C) to _____ (12°C, 13°C, 14°C) in _____ (3 h, 3.5 h, 4 h).

b) From B to C, the temperature _____ (increased, decreased) from _____ (11°C, 12°C, 13°C) to _____ (17°C, 18°C, 19°C) in _____ (5 h, 6 h, 7 h).

c) From C to D, the temperature _____ (increased, decreased) from _____ (14°C, 16°C, 18°C) to _____ (19°C, 21°C, 22°C) in _____ (2 h, 3 h, 4 h).

d) Describe what happened to the temperature from point D to E.

_____

e) From point E to F, the temperature _____ (increased, decreased) from _____ (19°C, 20°C, 21°C) to _____ (17°C, 18°C, 19°C) in _____ (4 h, 7 h, 9 h).

f) Between which segments did the temperature increase the fastest? Explain how you know.

_____

_____

5. The graph shows Nora's distance from home as she rides her bike. Describe the motion of the graph.

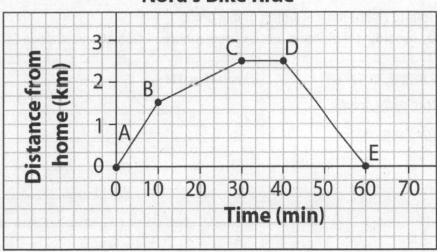

Nora's Bike Ride

a) Describe the first segment of the graph.

_____

b) Describe the second segment of the graph.

_____

c) Describe the third segment of the graph. Suggest a reason that might explain this segment of the graph.

| **Tip** |
| Read the example in the quick review if you need help. |

_____
_____
_____
_____

d) Describe the fourth segment of the graph.

_____
_____

e) What was the furthest point away from home on Nora's bike ride?

_____

f) In total, how far did Nora travel?

_____

In Your Words

Here are some of the important mathematical words of this unit.
Build your own glossary by recording definitions and examples here. The first one is done for you.

scatter plot *a set of data points on a graph*
For example, this scatter plot shows a
relationship between the time and
distance travelled.

Distance Travelled Over Time

curve of best fit _____

trend _____

linear relation _____

line of best fit _____

non-linear relation _____

List other mathematical words you need to know.

_____

Chapter Review

1.

Airliners

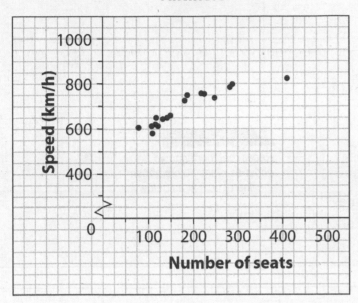

a) The scatter plot shows _____

b) Describe any trends in the data.
Explain your answer.

_____

_____

c) How many seats are on the fastest airliner shown on the graph?

_____

d) The speed of an airliner with 250 seats is about _____.

e) Why do you think airliners with more seats tend to have higher speeds?

_____

_____

2. The scatter plot shows the number of rose bushes in neighbourhood rose gardens.

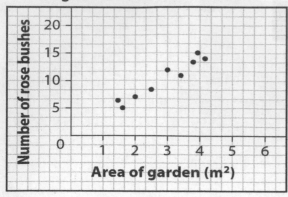

a) Draw a line of best fit.

> **Tip**
>
> *Recall that there should be about as many points above the line of best fit as below it.*

b) Are there any trends in the data?
    If yes, explain what the trend shows.

_____

_____

c) There are about _____ in a 5-m² garden.

d) Explain how you estimated the number of rose bushes in question c.

_____

_____

e) A garden that has 12 rose bushes is about _____.

3. Radioactive materials decay by emitting particles.
    The graph shows the number of particles a radioactive material emitted over time.

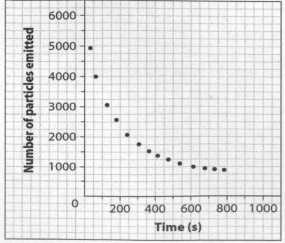

a) Describe any trends in the data.

_____

_____

b) Draw a line or curve of best fit.
   Explain how you decided which to draw.

_____

_____

c) There are about _____ emitted after 300 s.

d) There are about _____ emitted after 900 s.

e) Estimate the amount of time it takes for approximately 4000 particles to be emitted.

_____

5.4 **4.** When setting up a freshwater aquarium, some experts recommend adding 1 small fish for every 4 L of water in the tank.

a) Complete the table of values to show how many fish experts recommend keeping in a tank ranging in volume from 4 L to 28 L.

Number of fish	Water volume (L)
	4
	8
	12
	16
	20
	24
	28

Freshwater Aquarium

b) Graph the data.

c) Does the graph show a linear relationship? Justify your answer.

_____

_____

> **Tip**
> A linear relationship is a straight line.

d) Samantha can safely keep _____ in a 20-L tank.

e) If Joe has 7 small fish, his tank should be _____.

5. The table shows the relation of the volume of a sphere to the radius.

Radius (cm)	Volume (cm³)
0	0.0
2	33.5
4	268.0
6	904.3
8	2143.6
10	4186.7

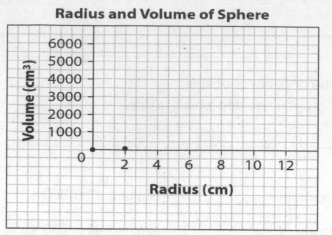

Radius and Volume of Sphere

a) Graph the data.

b) Describe any trends in the graph.

_____

c) Does the graph show a linear relationship? Justify your answer.

_____

d) The volume of a sphere with radius 5 cm is about _____.

e) A sphere has volume 3000 cm³.
Estimate the radius.

_____

6. The graph shows Sheri's distance from home as she walks to the post office and back. Describe her walk.

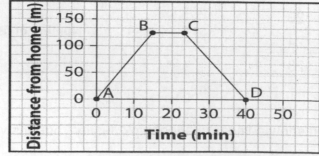

Sheri's Walk to the Post Office

From A to B, Sheri walks _____. She walks _____ in _____. From B to C, Sheri's distance from home _____. Sheri is at the post office for _____. From C to D, Sheri walks _____. She walks _____ in _____. She walks a total of _____ in _____.

Just for Fun

Truly Canadian

Plot the following points.
Join the points in order. Then join **y** to **a**.
Colour your graph.

a)	(7, 2)	b)	(7, 5)	c)	(4, 5)	d)	(5, 6)	e)	(1, 10)
f)	(2, 10)	g)	(1, 12)	h)	(3, 11)	i)	(3, 12)	j)	(6, 10)
k)	(5, 15)	l)	(7, 14)	m)	(8, 16)	n)	(9, 14)	o)	(11, 15)
p)	(10, 10)	q)	(13, 12)	r)	(13, 11)	s)	(15, 12)	t)	(14, 10)
u)	(15, 10)	v)	(11, 6)	w)	(12, 5)	x)	(9, 5)	y)	(9, 2)

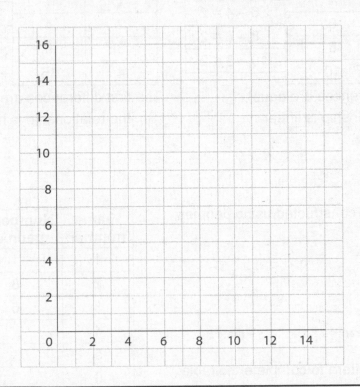

Quick Review

Tip

Join data points with a broken line or broken curve to see if there is a data trend.

➤ The first differences for a linear relation are equal.
  The points on a graph of a linear relation lie on a straight line.

➤ Non-linear relations have first differences that are not equal.
  The points on a graph of a non-linear relation do not lie on a straight line.

➤ You can determine whether a relation is linear from its table of values.

Frame 1   Frame 2   Frame 3   Frame 1   Frame 2   Frame 3

Frame number	Perimeter (units)	First differences (units)
1	4	
2	6	6 – 4 = 2
3	8	8 – 6 = 2
4	10	10 – 8 = 2

Frame number	Area (square units)	First differences (square units)
1	1	
2	4	4 – 1 = 3
3	9	9 – 4 = 5
4	16	16 – 9 = 7

The first differences are equal.
So, the relationship is linear.

The first differences are not equal.
So, the relationship is non-linear.

Practice

1. This pattern was constructed using pennies.

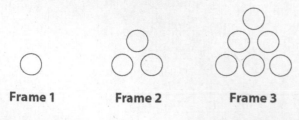

Frame 1   Frame 2   Frame 3

Frame number	Number of pennies	First differences
1	1	
2	3	3 – 1 = 2
3	6	6 – 3 =
4		
5		
6		

a) Extend the pattern to complete the table.

b) Is the relation linear or non-linear?

2. For each table below, determine the first differences.

Does the data represent a linear or non-linear relationship? Explain how you know.

a)

Number of Items	Cost ($)	First differences
1	3	
2	6	6 – 3 = 3
3	9	
4	12	
5	15	

b)

Time (s)	Height (cm)	First differences
0	1	
1	3	
2	7	
3	13	
4	21	

_____

_____

_____

_____

3. Tara has $1000 in her savings account.

Each week, she puts $150 of her pay into the account.

The table shows the balance in the account after 5 weeks.

a) Determine the first differences and complete the table.
What do the first differences represent?

_____

_____

_____

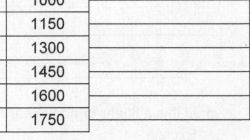

Time (weeks)	Balance ($)	First differences
0	1000	
1	1150	
2	1300	
3	1450	
4	1600	
5	1750	

b) Is the relation linear or non-linear?
Justify your answer.

_____

_____

_____

c) Graph *Time* against *Balance*.
Does the graph support your answer to part b?
Explain.

_____

_____

_____

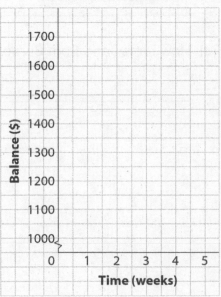

Tara's Account Balance

4. Jane is driving from London to Barrie.
The table shows her distance from Barrie in kilometres.

Time (min)	Distance (km)	First differences
0	250	200 − 250 =
30	200	
60	150	
90	100	
120	50	
150	0	

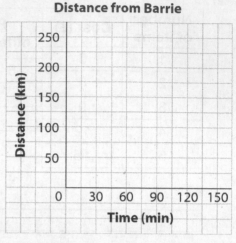

Distance from Barrie

a) By how much are the numbers in the first column increasing?

_____

b) Determine the first differences and complete the table.
What do the first differences represent?

_____

_____

c) Is this a linear or non-linear relation?
Explain.

_____

d) How far is Jane from Barrie after driving for 75 min?

_____

Quick Review

➤ You can draw a distance-time graph to show how the distance changes over time during a trip.

Rick and Beni decided to hike from their campsite to Clear Lake.
This graph is a distance-time graph of their hiking trip.

The graph is linear.

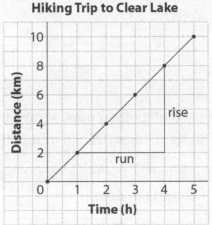

Hiking Trip to Clear Lake

To determine Rick and Beni's average speed, recall that:

Average speed = $\dfrac{\text{Distance travelled}}{\text{Time taken}}$

Choose any two points on the line:
(1, 2) and (4, 8)

The vertical distance between the points on the line, or the **rise**, tells you the distance travelled.
The rise is: 8 km – 2 km = 6 km

The horizontal distance between the points, or the **run**, tells you how much time it took.
The run is: 4 h – 1 h = 3 h

Average speed = $\dfrac{\text{Distance travelled}}{\text{Time taken}}$

$= \dfrac{\text{rise}}{\text{run}}$

$= \dfrac{6 \text{ km}}{3 \text{ h}}$

$= 2 \text{ km/h}$

Their average hiking speed was 2 km/h.

$\dfrac{\text{rise}}{\text{run}}$ is called the **rate of change**.

The rate of change tells you how many units to move up or down for every unit you move to the right on the graph.
The rate of change of distance over time is the average speed.

Practice

1. Patrick plotted a distance-time graph for a passenger train.
   Determine the rate of change.

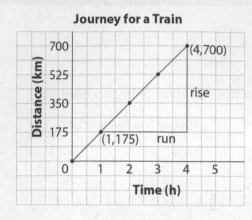

Journey for a Train

The rise is: 700 km – _____ km = _____ km

The run is: 4 h – _____ h = _____ h

Rate of change = $\dfrac{\text{rise}}{\text{run}}$

= $\dfrac{\text{____ km}}{\text{____ h}}$

= _____ km/h

The rate of change is _____ km/h.

2. A herd of caribou runs across the tundra to a water source.
   The herd takes 10 min to run 10 km.

   a) Complete the table to show the distance the herd travels at 10-min intervals.
      Graph the data.

Time (min)	Distance (km)
0	0
10	
20	
30	
40	

   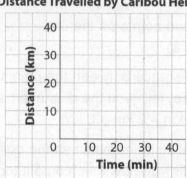

   Distance Travelled by Caribou Herd

   b) How far does the herd travel after 35 min?

   Hint

   Find the point on the line at time 35 min. Read the vertical distance on the graph at that point.

   _____

   c) Determine the rate of change to 1 decimal place.

3. Brandon ran in a 5-km cross-country race. It took him 15 min to run 2.5 km.

a) Complete the table to show Brandon's distance from the starting line at 15-min intervals. Graph the data.

Time (min)	Distance (km)
0	
15	
30	

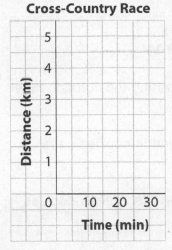

Cross-Country Race

b) What is the rate of change of distance over time?
   Give your answer to 1 decimal place.

> **Tip**
> Use any 2 points on the line to find the rise and run.

c) What was Brandon's average speed for his race?
   How do you know?

_____

_____

d) What was Brandon's average speed in kilometres per hour?

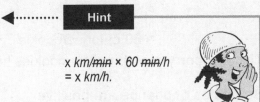

Hint

x km/min × 60 min/h
= x km/h.

_____

Quick Review

Dean and Paul were comparing the nutrition labels on their cookie packages.

Two of Dean's chocolate-fudge cookies have 150 calories.

Three of Paul's raspberry-marshmallow cookies have 180 calories.

Calories in Cookies

For Dean's chocolate-fudge cookies:
To find the rate of change,
choose any two points on the line: (2, 150) and (4, 300).
The rise is: 300 calories – 150 calories = 150 calories
The run is: 4 cookies – 2 cookies = 2 cookies

$$\text{Rate of change} = \frac{\text{rise}}{\text{run}}$$

$$= \frac{150 \text{ calories}}{2 \text{ cookies}}$$

$$= 75 \text{ calories/cookie}$$

Dean's chocolate-fudge cookies have 75 calories per cookie.

For Paul's raspberry-marshmallow cookies:
To find the rate of change, choose any two points on the line: (1, 60) and (3, 180).
The rise is: 180 calories – 60 calories = 120 calories
The run is: 3 cookies – 1 cookie = 2 cookies

$$\text{Rate of change} = \frac{\text{rise}}{\text{run}}$$

$$= \frac{120 \text{ calories}}{2 \text{ cookies}}$$

$$= 60 \text{ calories/cookie}$$

The raspberry-marshmallow cookies have 60 calories per cookie.

Both rates of change are positive.
The cookie with more calories has a greater rate of change and a steeper line on the graph.

Practice

1. Use the graphs to determine each rate of change.

a) **Purchasing Ballet Tickets**

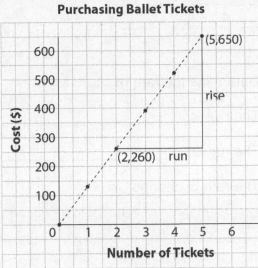

b) **Carbohydrates in Cookies**

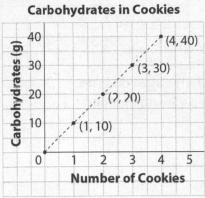

Tip

Use any 2 points on the line to find the rise and run.

Rise: $650 – _____ = _____   Rise: _____

Run: 5 tickets – _____ = _____   Run: _____

Rate of change = $\frac{rise}{run}$ Rate of change =

2. A 5.8-cm votive candle takes 15 h to burn down completely.
   Use the graph to determine the rate of change to 1 decimal place.
   Is the rate of change positive or negative?

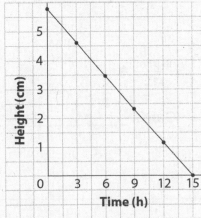

Burning a Votive Candle

Sample Answer

To find the rate of change, choose any two

points on the line: _____

The rise is: _____

The run is: _____

Rate of change = $\frac{rise}{run}$

_____

_____

3. Derek purchased a pool for his backyard.

He must fill the pool with water before he and his friends can use it.

The table shows how fast the pool fills.

Time (h)	0	1	2	3	4	5
Volume (L)	0	3263	6526			

a) Graph volume against time.

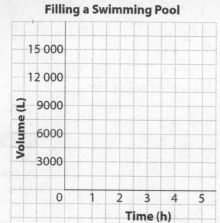

Filling a Swimming Pool

b) Determine the rate of change.

The rise is: _____

The run is: _____

The rate of change   =

4. Tyler wants to buy a fuel-efficient car.

The fuel consumption for 3 different cars is shown in the table.

Car	Amount of fuel used (L)	Distance driven (km)
A	55	880
B	82	1100
C	42	850

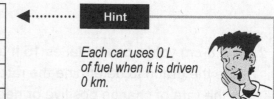

Hint

Each car uses 0 L of fuel when it is driven 0 km.

a) Determine the rates of change for the 3 makes of cars.
   Give your answer to 1 decimal place where necessary.

$\frac{880 \text{ km}}{55 \text{ L}} =$

$\frac{1100 \text{ km}}{82 \text{ L}} \doteq$

$\frac{850 \text{ km}}{42 \text{ L}} \doteq$

Car A: _____

Car B: _____

Car C: _____

b) What do these rates of change represent?

_____

_____

c) Which car should Tyler buy, and why?

_____

Quick Review

Direct variation is shown on a graph as a straight line that passes through the origin (0, 0).

When two quantities vary directly, they are *proportional*.

On this graph, the mass *varies directly* with the *number* of cookies.

So, the mass is *directly proportional* to the number of cookies.

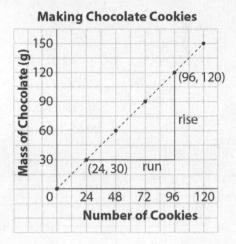

Making Chocolate Cookies

> You can write rules and solve problems using direct variation.

Determine the rate of change to write a rule.
Choose any two points on the graph: (24, 30) and (96, 120)
The rise is: 120 g – 30 g = 90 g
The run is: 96 cookies – 24 cookies = 72 cookies

$$\frac{\text{rise}}{\text{run}} = \frac{90 \text{ g}}{72 \text{ cookies}}$$
$$= 1.25 \text{ g/cookie}$$

The rate of change is the mass of chocolate in one cookie.

The mass of chocolate needed = (1.25) × (number of cookies)

                  ↑   ↑

       the rate of change   the number
       in grams per cookie   of cookies

Use this rule to determine how much chocolate is needed to make 48 cookies.

Number of cookies that can be made = 1.25 × 48
                                     = 60

To make 48 cookies, 60 g of chocolate is needed.

Practice

1. Does each graph represent direct variation?
   Explain how you know.

   a)
   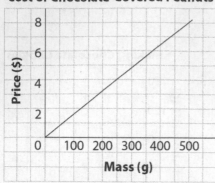
   Cost of Chocolate-Covered Peanuts

   b)
   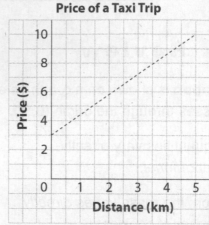
   Price of a Taxi Trip

   _____   _____

   _____   _____

2. Alex and her friends Kayla and Laura are buying trail mix at the bulk-food store.
   The table shows how many grams each girl bought and how much it cost.

Cost ($)	1.67	5.00	3.33
Mass (g)	100	300	200

   Hint
   Draw a line through the data points and see if it passes through the origin (0, 0).

   a) Graph the data.

   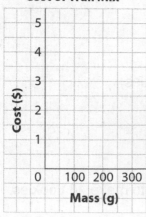
   Cost of Trail Mix

   b) Does the graph represent direct variation?
      Justify your answer.

      _____

      _____

   c) What is the rate of change?
      Give your answer to 3 decimal places.

      $$\frac{\$5.00 - \$1.67}{300\ g - 100\ g} =$$

      _____

   d) Write a rule to determine the cost of trail mix.

      _____

   e) Use the rule to determine how much it would cost to buy 500 g of trail mix.

      _____

146

3. Jeff got a new job at a hamburger stand.
   The table shows how much he will get paid depending on the number of hours he works.

Time worked (h)	5	10	15	20	25	30
Pay ($)	45	90	135	180	225	270

a) Graph Jeff's earnings.
   Does the graph represent direct variation? Justify your answer.

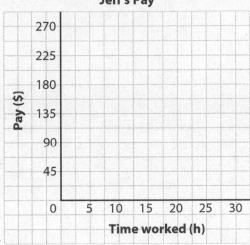

_____

_____

_____

_____

_____

b) What is the rate of change?
   What does it represent?

_____

c) Write a rule to determine Jeff's pay.

   Pay in $ = _____ × time worked in hours

d) Write an equation to determine Jeff's pay _P_ when he works _h_ hours.

   $P =$ _____

e) Use the equation to determine how much Jeff will earn if he works 40 h.

_____

4. Melanie teaches piano lessons.

The table shows how much she will get paid depending on the number of hours she teaches.

Time worked (h)	2	4	6	8
Pay ($)	90	180	270	360

a) Graph Melanie's earnings.

Does the graph represent direct variation? Justify your answer.

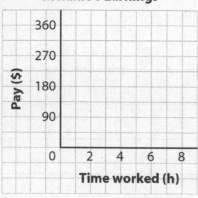

Melanie's Earnings

_____

_____

b) What is the rate of change?

What does it represent?

_____

c) Write an equation to determine Melanie's pay *P* when she works *t* hours.

P = _____

e) Use the equation to determine how much Melanie will earn if she works 20 h.

_____

Quick Review

Shandi bought a piñata for her younger sister's birthday party.
The piñata cost $15.00.
She spent $1.50 per child on party favours
to put in the piñata.
This graph shows the cost of the piñata
for up to 10 children.

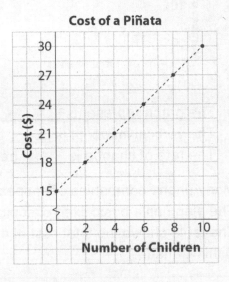

Cost of a Piñata

Join the data points with a broken line since
you cannot have a fraction of a child.
All points lie on a straight line.
The graph does *not* pass through the origin.

This illustrates **partial variation**.
The total cost of the piñata is the sum of a
fixed cost and a variable cost.

The point where the line crosses the vertical axis is the **vertical intercept**.
On this graph, the vertical intercept is $15.00.
It represents the cost of the piñata without any candy in it.

➢ You can determine the rate of change for a partial variation situation.
    The rise is: $27.00 – $18.00 = $9.00
    The run is: 8 children – 2 children = 6 children
    The rate of change is: $\frac{\text{rise}}{\text{run}} = \frac{\$9.00}{6 \text{ children}}$
                       = $1.50/child
    The rate of change is equal to the cost of the party favours for each child.

➢ You can write an equation to represent the situation.
    Cost of the piñata in $ = 15 + (1.50 × number of children)

                fixed cost   variable cost

Let *C* represent the cost in dollars.
Let *n* represent the number of children.
Then, $C = 15.00 + 1.50n$

    vertical intercept   rate of change

Practice

1. Do the following graphs represent direct variation?
   Explain how you know.

a)

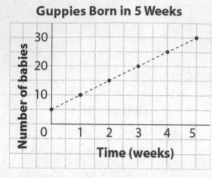

Guppies Born in 5 Weeks

The graph represents _____ variation.

The vertical intercept is _____ babies.

The rate of change is _____ babies/week.

b)

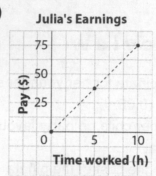

Julia's Earnings

The graph represents _____ variation.

The vertical intercept is _____.

The rate of change is _____.

2. Many phone companies offer special long-distance calling plans.
   The plan has a basic fixed cost plus a variable cost.
   The table shows the total cost of a plan with *Talk-a-lot* long-distance service for calls within Canada.

Cost ($)	1.00	1.40	1.80	2.20	2.60	3.00
Length of call (min)	100	110	120	130	140	150

a) Graph *Cost* against *Length of call*.

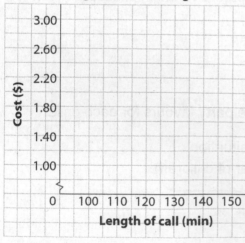

Long-Distance Calling

b) Does the graph represent partial variation? Explain.

_____

_____

c) What is the rate of change?
   What does it represent?

_____

_____

_____

d) Determine the total cost for a 170-min call.

_____

150

3. Adam runs a tiling company.

He charges a $450 fixed cost, plus $3.25 per tile.

a) Write an equation to determine the cost in dollars, *C*, for the number of tiles, *n*.

The cost is: $_____ + ($_____ × number of tiles).   ◀ ········· **Hint**

The equation is: ___ = ____ + ____ × ____

Total cost = fixed cost +
variable cost

b) What does Adam charge for installing 480 tiles?

_____

4. Dante has a wireless high-speed Internet plan for his laptop.

He pays $60 for one month of service which includes
30 MB of uploaded or downloaded data.
It costs $6 for every additional megabyte of data
uploaded or downloaded during the month.

Wireless Internet Plan

a) Graph *Cost* against *Extra Data*.

b) What is the fixed cost?

_____

c) What is the rate of change?
What does the rate of change represent?

_____

_____

d) Write an equation that describes this linear relation.

_____

_____

e) How much would it cost to download 39 MB of data in 1 month?

◀ ········· **Hint**

First determine how
much extra data is
used.

_____

Quick Review

This graph represents Michael's earnings delivering pizza.

He is paid $6.50 for each hour he works.

His pay varies directly with the number of hours he works.

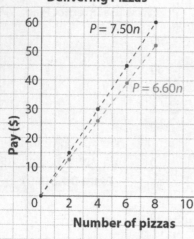

Delivering Pizzas

$P = 7.50n$

$P = 6.60n$

The rate of change is: $6.50/h.

The rule is: Earnings in dollars = 6.50 × number of hours worked.

Let P represent Michael's earnings in dollars.

Let n represent the number of hours worked.

Then the equation is: $P = 6.50n$

Michael is given a raise.

He now earns $7.50 for each hour he works.

The rate of change is now $7.50/h.

The new rule is: Earnings in dollars = 7.50 × number of hours worked.

The new equation is: $P = 7.50n$

Both graphs pass through the origin and go up to the right.

The graph of Michael's new pay has the greater rate of change.

The line for the new rate of change is steeper than the line for the old rate of change.

Beyond the origin, the line for the new rate of change lies above the line for the old rate of change.

Practice

1. Does each situation represent direct variation or partial variation? Explain how you know.

   a) Vishnu is paid $11/h as a grocery clerk.

   _____

   _____

   b) The cost to go bowling is $3.00 to rent shoes, plus $24.00 per hour.

   _____

   _____

2. Match each graph with the most appropriate equation. Explain how you know.

   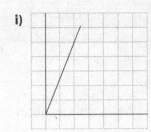

   a) $C = 50n$
      The vertical intercept is 0.
      The graph represents _____ variation.
      The equation has the _____ rate of change.
      The matching graph is _____.

   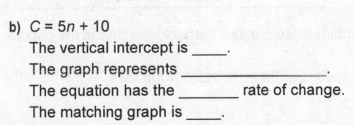

   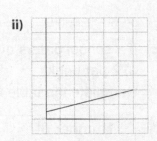

   b) $C = 5n + 10$
      The vertical intercept is _____.
      The graph represents _____.
      The equation has the _____ rate of change.
      The matching graph is _____.

   c) $C = 5n$

   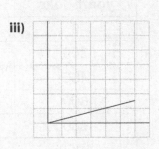

   The matching graph is _____.

   d) $C = 5n + 40$

   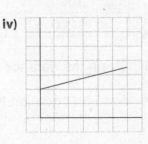

   The matching graph is _____.

2. Memories Yearbooks wants to sell their yearbooks to Abelard High School. The yearbooks cost $25 per book for orders up to 1000 yearbooks.

a) Complete the table to show the total cost for up to 1000 yearbooks. Graph the data.

Number of yearbooks	Cost ($)
0	0
200	5000
400	
600	
800	
1000	

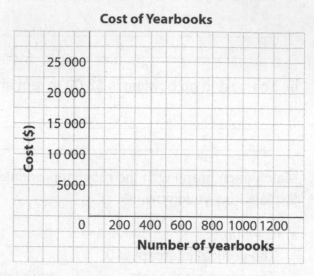

Cost of Yearbooks

b) Write an equation to determine the cost of the yearbooks.

_____

c) If a school orders over 1000 yearbooks, Memories Yearbooks discounts the cost to $22 per book.
Complete the table for the discounted cost for up to 1200 yearbooks.

Number of yearbooks	Cost ($)
0	0
200	
400	
600	
800	
1000	
1200	

d) Graph the data for the discounted cost on the grid in part a.

e) Write an equation to determine the discounted cost of the yearbooks.

_____

154

3. Grandma Erwin is going to the local fall fair.
   The admission fee for senior citizens is $7.
   A strip of ride tickets cost $10.

   a) Complete the table to show the total cost up to 4 strips of tickets.
      Graph the data.

Strips of tickets	Cost ($)
0	7
1	
2	
3	
4	

   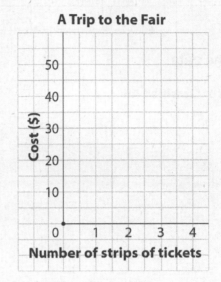

   A Trip to the Fair

   b) Write an equation to determine the cost of Grandma Erwin going to the fair.

   _____

   c) Grandma and Granddad Erwin both decided to go to the fair.
      They brought their 8-year-old granddaughter Theresina along.
      The admission fee for children under 12 is $2.
      Complete the table to show the total cost for up to 4 strips of tickets.

Strips of tickets	Cost ($)
0	16
1	
2	
3	
4	

   d) Graph the new data on the grid in part a.

   e) Write an equation to determine the total cost of going to the fair.

   _____

4. Kent wants to sell his motorcycle.
   He puts an ad in the local newspaper.
   The newspaper charges $42 each day if the ad is in the paper for 3 days or less.

   a) Make a table of Kent's cost to run the ad for up to 3 days.

Days	0	1	2	3
Cost ($)				

   b) Graph the data.

   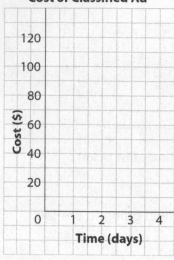

   Cost of Classified Ad

   c) Write an equation to determine Kent's cost.

   _____

   d) The newspaper gives a discount for ads that run for longer than 3 days.
      The cost for ads that run 4 days is $28.03 for each day.
      Complete the table for the discounted ad.

Days	0	1	2	3	4
Cost ($)					

   e) Write an equation to determine Kent's cost.

   _____

   e) How will this change the graph?

   _____

   f) Graph the data for the discounted ad.

Quick Review

Equations are like scales where everything must balance.
What you do to 1 side of the equation, you must also do to the other side.

You can use inverse operations to "undo"
the operations in an equation.

Operation	Inverse
Addition	Subtraction
Subtraction	Addition
Multiplication	Division
Division	Multiplication

To solve the equation $4x - 7 = 13$,
use the inverse operations to isolate x.

$$4x - 7 = 13$$
$$4x - 7 + 7 = 13 + 7 \quad \text{Add 7 to each side.}$$
$$4x = 20$$
$$\frac{4x}{4} = \frac{20}{4} \quad \text{Divide each side by 4.}$$
$$x = 5$$

The solution is $x = 5$.

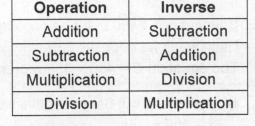

Hint

First undo addition and subtraction.

Then undo multiplication and division.

Practice

1. Write the equation represented by the balance scales.
   Explain how to solve the equation.

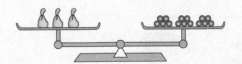

Let x represent the number of candies in each bag.
There are 3 bags in the left pan.
This is represented by the expression $3x$.
There are ___ candies in the right pan.
This is represented by the number ___.
So, the balance scales model the equation $3x = $ ___.

To solve the equation:
Divide the candies in the right pan into 3 equal groups.
Each group contains ___ candies.
So, each bag contains ___ candies.

The solution is $x = $ ___.

2. Solve each equation.

Tip

Use inverse operations to isolate x.

a) $x + 5 = 40$

$x + 5 - \underline{} = 40 - \underline{}$

$x = \underline{}$

b) $2x = 18$

$\frac{2x}{} = \frac{18}{}$

$x = \underline{}$

c) $4x - 17 = 15$

$4x - 17 + \underline{} = 15 + \underline{}$

$\frac{4x}{4} =$

$x = \underline{}$

3. Spencer has $450 in his savings account.
   Each week he deposits $35.
   The equation $S = 450 + 35n$ represents his total savings, S dollars, after n weeks.

a) How much will Spencer have saved after 12 weeks?

$S = 450 + 35n$

$= 450 + 35(\underline{})$

$= \underline{}$

b) Spencer wants to buy a dirt bike that costs $1325.
    How many weeks will it take him to have that amount in total savings?

$S = 450 + 35n$

$\underline{} = 450 + 35n$

$\underline{} - \underline{} = 450 + 35n - \underline{}$

$\underline{} = 35n$

$\underline{} = \frac{35n}{}$

$n = \underline{}$

4. Solve each equation.

a) $2x = 5$

$\frac{2x}{} = \frac{5}{}$

$x =$

◄ **Hint**

Whatever you do to 1 side of the equation, you must do to the other side.

b) $-3x + 5 = 23$

$x = \underline{}$

c) $9x + 7 = 52$

$x = \underline{}$

5. Shawna is having her birthday party at the movie theatre.
   The cost is $57 plus $14.25 for each guest.
   The equation $C = 57 + 14.25n$ represents the total cost, C dollars, for n guests.

   a) Shawna's mom told her she could invite 10 guests.
      What is the cost for 10 guests?

   _____

   b) The total bill for Shawna's party is $171.
      How many guests came to her party?

   _____

6. Nick joined the Canadian Armed Forces.
   When he is not wearing his pack, he weighs 77 kg.
   He packs 2 kg of rations for each day he is on an exercise.

   a) Write an equation to determine his total weight, W kg, for d days on an exercise.

   _____

   b) Nick is going on an exercise for 7 days.
      How much will the total weight be?

   _____

   c) Nick weighs himself with his pack just before he leaves on an exercise.
      The total weight is 99 kg.
      How many days will he be on an exercise?

   _____

Quick Review

While on a trip, Tammy drove at a rate of 80 km/h.
You can determine how long it took Tammy to travel 300 km using 3 different methods.

➤ You can make a table to show the time spent travelling and the distance travelled.

Time (h)	1	2	3	4	5
Distance (km)	80	160	240	320	400

From the table, it took her almost 4 h to travel 300 km.

➤ You can graph the data.

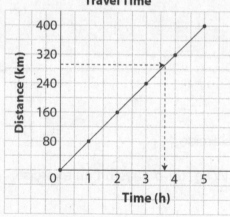

Travel Time

From the graph, it took her about 3.8 h to travel 300 km.

➤ You can use an equation to find the exact answer.
The equation of the line is: $D = 80t$.

$$D = 80t$$
$$300 = 80t$$
$$\frac{300}{80} = \frac{80t}{80}$$
$$3.75 = t$$

It took Tammy exactly 3.75 h to travel 300 km.

Practice

1. Kairin makes organic dog biscuits to sell.
   This table shows how much Kairin will earn if she sells up to 25 bags of dog biscuits.

Number of bags	0	5	10	15	20	25
Earnings ($)	0	32.50	65.00	97.50	130.00	162.50

a) Graph the data.

b) Use the graph to determine how much Kairin will earn if she sells 17 bags of dog biscuits.

_____

c) Use the graph to determine how many bags Kairin sold if she earned $78.00.

_____

2. When Jennifer went away to college, her grandmother deposited $5100 in Jennifer's bank account. Each month, Jennifer takes out $425 to pay her rent.

a) Write an equation for the balance in the account, B dollars, after n months.

   Balance = initial amount – (_____ × time in months)

   $B =$ _____ – _____ n

b) How many months will Jennifer be able to pay her rent?

   ◄·········· | Hint |

   Use the equation and set B = 0.

   Jennifer will be able to pay her rent for _____ months.

3. When you are physically active, your heart rate increases. It is important that your heart rate does not exceed a maximum rate.

   According to heart specialists, the relation between the maximum heart rate, p beats per minute, and your age, a years, is represented by the equation $p = 220 - a$.

   a) Complete the following table for maximum heart rate.

Age (years)	15	25	35	45	55
Maximum heart rate (beats/min)	205				

   b) What is the maximum heart rate for someone 30 years old?

   The maximum heart rate for someone 30 years old is _____.

4. It is a distance of 3525 km from where Taran lives in Toronto, Ontario to where his cousins live in Edmonton, Alberta.

   Taran decided to drive to Edmonton for a visit, travelling 850 km each day.

   a) Complete the table. Graph the data.

Time (days)	Distance (km)
0	0
1	
2	
3	
4	
5	

   b) Use the graph to determine approximately how long it took Taran to travel to Edmonton.

   _____

   c) Write an equation to determine the distance, D kilometres, after t days.

   _____

   d) Use the equation to determine how many days it will take Taran to travel to Edmonton. Give your answer to 3 decimal places.
   How does your answer compare to your answer in part b?

   _____

   _____

6.9 Solving Problems Involving Linear Relations

Quick Review

Patrick borrows $3000 from his parents to buy a new car.
He plans to pay his parents the same amount each month until the loan is paid off.

➤ Determine the rate of change from the graph.
After 3 months, Patrick owes $2250.
After 6 months, he owes $1500.
The rise is: $1500 – $2250 = –$750
The run is: 6 months – 3 months = 3 months

Rate of change = $\dfrac{\text{rise}}{\text{run}}$

$= \dfrac{-\$750}{3\ \text{months}}$

$= -\$250/\text{month}$

So, Patrick's payments are $250 each month.

Patrick's Loan Repayments

➤ Write an equation.
The vertical intercept is $3000.
The vertical intercept represents the amount that Patrick borrowed.
Amount owed = $3000 – ($250/month × time in months)
Let *A* dollars represent the amount owed and *t* months represent the time.
$A = 3000 - 250t$

When Patrick pays off his loan, the amount he owes is $0.
You can determine when Patrick will have paid off his loan in two ways.

➤ Use the graph
At 12 months, the amount owed is zero.
This means Patrick will have paid off the loan after 12 months.

➤ Use the equation.
$0 = 3000 - 250t$
$250t = 3000 - 250t + 250t$
$250t = 3000$
$\dfrac{250t}{250} = \dfrac{3000}{250}$
$t = 12$
Patrick will have paid off the loan after 12 months.

Practice

1. This graph models the motion of a snowmobile.
Make a table of values for this graph.

Time (h)	Distance (km)
0	0
1	50

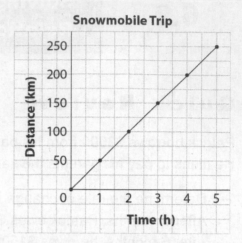

Snowmobile Trip

2. This graph shows the cost of an electrician per hour.

a) Use the graph to complete the table of values.

Time (h)	Cost ($)
0	
1	

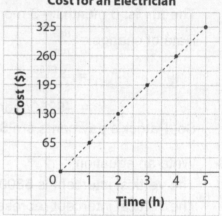

Cost for an Electrician

b) Write an equation that relates the total cost, C dollars, to the time, t hours.

The situation is modelled by _____ variation.

Rule: _____

Rate of change = $\frac{\text{rise}}{\text{run}}$

=

=

Equation: _____

c) How much does it cost if the electrician works 15 h?

_____

3. The volume of blood a heart can pump in 1 min is called its cardiac output. At rest, a greyhound's heart pumps 200 mL of blood per minute for every kilogram of weight.

a) Complete the table for greyhounds weighing from 27 kg to 30 kg. Graph the data.

Weight (kg)	Blood pumped (mL/min)
27	
28	
29	
30	

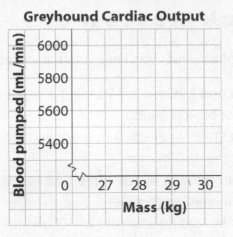

Greyhound Cardiac Output

b) Use the table to write an equation that relates the blood pumped, B mL/min, to the weight of the greyhound, w kg.

_____

c) How much blood is pumped in 1 min by the heart of a greyhound weighing 30 kg?

_____

d) What is the weight of a greyhound whose heart pumps 6400 mL of blood per minute?

Tip
Use the equation you created in part b.

_____

e) When racing, a greyhound's heart rate increases to 1000 mL/min per kilogram of body weight.
Write an equation that relates the blood pumped while racing, R mL/min, to the weight of the greyhound, w kg.

_____

f) How much blood would the heart of a racing greyhound weighing 29 kg pump per minute?

_____

165

Quick Review

The point at which two lines cross is called the point of intersection.

Douglas and Melissa are running along a 500-m section of bicycle path.
Douglas starts at the 500-m mark and Melissa starts at the 100-m mark.
They start running at the same time and are running toward each other.
Douglas is running at a rate of 100 m/min and Melissa is running at a rate of 80 m/min.

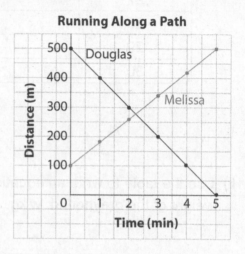

Running Along a Path

➤ You can use the graph to determine where and when they will meet.
  The lines intersect at approximately (2.25, 280).
  Douglas and Melissa meet after running for 2.25 min, 280 m along the bicycle path.

Practice

1. Jacob left home driving at 80 km/h on the way to his cottage.
   Angela followed 30 min later, driving in the same direction at 100 km/h.

   a) Complete the table for times up to 150 min. Graph the data.

Time (min)	Jacob's Distance (km)	Angela's Distance (km)
0	0	0
30	40	0
60		50
90		
120		
150		

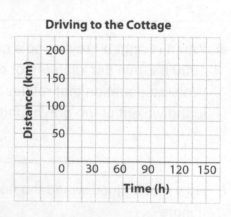

Driving to the Cottage

   b) Where do the lines intersect? What does this point represent?

   _____

   _____

2. The Student Council is planning a dance.
   The cost to throw the dance will be $100 for decorations and $500 for a DJ, plus $5 per person for finger foods and soft drinks.
   a) Write an equation that relates the total cost, C dollars, to the number of people, n.

   This situation represents _____ variation.
   Total cost in $ = $_____ + $____/person × (number of people)
   $C = $ _____ + ____ × n

   b) Revenue is the money the Student Council receives from the tickets they sell.
   Tickets to the dance cost $6 each. Write an equation that relates the total revenue, R dollars, to the number of tickets sold, n.

   This situation represents _____ variation.
   Total revenue in $ = _____
   $R = $ _____

   c) Make a table of values for each equation.

   $C = 600 + 5n$

Number of people	0	300	400	500	600	700
Cost ($)						

   $R = 6n$

Number of people	0	300	400	500	600	700
Revenue ($)						

   d) Graph the data.

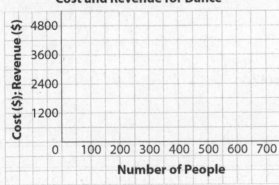

Cost and Revenue for Dance

   e) Where do the lines intersect? What does this point represent?

   _____

   _____

3. Your school is selling T-shirts to promote school spirit.
   The school has asked 2 companies for prices to make the T-shirts.
   Company A charges $100.00 fixed cost, plus $3.65 per shirt.
   Company B charges $4.25 per shirt.

   a) Write an equation for the total cost in dollars, C, for number of T-shirts, n, for each company.

   Company A: $C =$ _____   Company B: $C =$ _____

   b) Make a table of values for each equation.

   Company A

Number of T-shirts	0	100	200	300	400
Cost ($)					

   Company B

Number of T-shirts	0	100	200	300	400
Cost ($)					

   c) Graph the data on the same grid.

   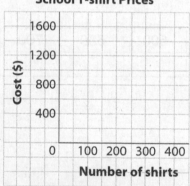

   d) Approximately where do the lines intersect?
      What does this point represent?

      _____

      _____

   e) Who has the best price for 100 T-shirts?

      _____

   f) Who has the best price for 300 T-shirts?

      _____

In Your Words

Here are some of the important mathematical words from this chapter.
Build your own glossary by recording definitions and examples here. The first one is done for you.

linear relation _a relation that can be represented by a straight line graph_

_____

_____

_____

rise _____

_____

_____

_____

_____

run _____

_____

_____

_____

_____

rate of change _____

_____

_____

_____

_____

direct variation _____

_____

_____

_____

_____

partial variation _____

_____

_____

_____

_____

List other mathematical words you need to know.

_____

1. The table shows the cost to rent a steam cleaner for different lengths of time.

Time (days)	Cost ($)	First differences
2	27.50	
3	55.00	
4	82.50	
5	110.00	
6	137.50	
7	165.00	

a) Determine the first differences and complete the table.
   What do the first differences represent?

   _____

   _____

b) Is the relation linear or non-linear?

   _____

2.

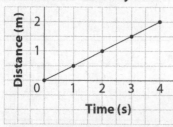

Distance Rolled by Ball

a) Determine the rate of change from the graph.

   _____

b) Write an equation for this relation.

   _____

c) Does this graph represent direct or partial variation?

   _____

3. a) Determine the rate of change from the graph.

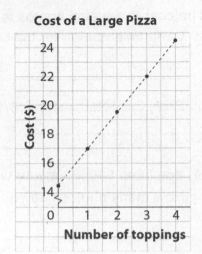

Cost of a Large Pizza

_____

b) Write an equation for this relation.

_____

c) Does this graph represent direct or partial variation?

_____

6.5
6.6
4. Reem buys a lot of books. She's thinking of joining her bookstore's membership club. It costs $25 to join the club, and members get a 10% discount on all books.

a) Complete the table of values for the amount of money Reem would spend on books with and without the membership.

Book price ($)	0	100	200	300	400
Amount spent without membership ($)					
Amount spent with membership ($)					

b) Graph the data.

c) Write an equation that relates the amount spent without a membership, A dollars, and book price, p.

_____

d) Write an equation that relates the amount spent with a membership, A dollars, and book price, p.

_____

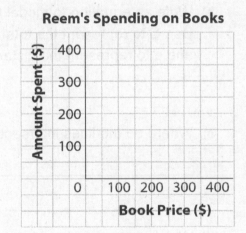

Reem's Spending on Books

6.7
5. Solve each equation.

a) $5x + 3 = 8$

b) $-3x + 2 = 11$

c) $20 - 4x = 4$

$x =$ _____

$x =$ _____

$x =$ _____

6. The cost to develop photos is $2.00 for the service plus $0.29 for each photo.

   a) Write an equation for the cost, C dollars for n photos.

   _____

   b) Does this relationship represent direct variation or partial variation?

   _____

   c) You have $10.00 in your wallet.
   How many photos can you get developed with the money you have?

   _____

7. Karen wants to rent a moving truck for 1 day.
   She is comparing prices from 2 rental companies.
   Company A charges $40.00 plus $0.49 per kilometre.
   Company B charges $71.00 plus $0.18 per kilometre.

   a) Complete the table for distances up to 300 km. Graph the data.

Distance (km)	Company A Cost ($)	Company B Cost ($)
0		
100		
200		
300		

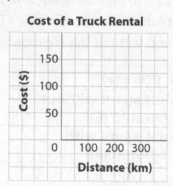

Cost of a Truck Rental

   b) Write an equation to model the cost for each company.
   Use C to represent the total cost in dollars
   and d to represent the distance in kilometres.

   c) Where do the lines intersect? What does this point represent?

   _____

   _____

   d) Which company should Karen choose if she is moving 50 km away?
   Explain your choice.

   _____

   _____

Just for Fun

Euclid's Game

A Game for 2

Euclid was a Greek mathematician who lived from 325–265 BC. He invented this subtraction game. You will need a piece of paper to play.

Pairs of starting numbers: 25 and 19; 42 and 32; 50 and 14; 66 and 36.

Player A picks a pair of starting numbers from the pairs above and writes them on a piece of paper. Then, the player finds the difference between the 2 numbers (the difference must always be positive) and writes the answer on the paper with the first 2 numbers.

Player B chooses any 2 of the 3 numbers written on the paper, finds the difference, and writes the answer on the paper with the other 3 numbers. If the answer is a number that is already written on the paper, the player must find the difference between 2 other numbers. The player keeps working until an answer is found that isn't written on the paper.

Player A chooses any 2 of those 4 numbers, and play continues until there are no new numbers left to use. The winner is the player who wrote down the last number.

Heads and Tails

Place 8 coins face down on a table. Determine the least number of moves it takes to show 8 heads. For each move, turn over any 3 coins.

Remember that you must turn over 3 <u>different</u> coins for each move.

Record each move you make, using T for tails and H for heads.

_____

_____

Quick Review

Algebra tiles can be used to represent algebraic expressions.

Positive tiles   Negative tiles

1 x x^2 -1 $-x$ $-x^2$

Pairs of opposite tiles add to zero, so we call them **zero pairs**.

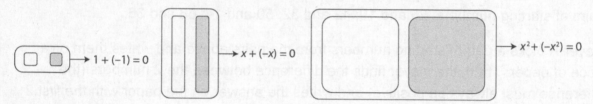

$\rightarrow 1 + (-1) = 0$ $\rightarrow x + (-x) = 0$ $\rightarrow x^2 + (-x^2) = 0$

The expression $-x^2 - 2x + 3 + 2x^2 - x$ can be represented by the following tiles:

This expression has five **terms**: $-x^2$, $-2x$, 3, $2x^2$, $-x$.

Like terms are represented by tiles that have the same shape. By grouping the like tiles, we can remove the zero pairs to simplify the expression.

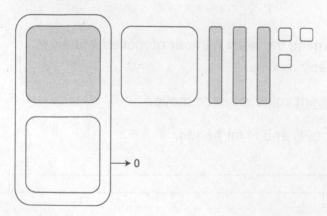

$\rightarrow 0$

The expression can be written as $x^2 - 3x + 3$.

Practice

1. Circle the expression that represents each group of algebra tiles.

a)

$-2x^2 + 2x + 1$
$2x^2 - 2x - 1$
$3x^2 + 5x - 4$

b)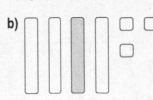

$-x^2 + 2x + 3$
$2x + 3$
$2x + 2x + 3$

2. Model each expression by shading the appropriate algebra tiles.

a) $x^2 - 8$

b) $4x - 1$

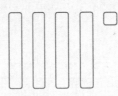

c) $x^2 - x + 1$

d) $-2x^2 + 5x - 7$

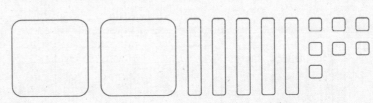

3. a) True or false: $2x$ and $4x$ are terms that are like $5x$.
   How do you know?

   _____

   _____

   b) True or false: $9x$ and $3x^2$ are terms that are like $7x^2$.
      How do you know?

   _____

4. In each part, write the expression represented by the group of algebra tiles. Then combine like terms and write the simplified expression.

◀ ········

a)

= __ x^2 − __ x^2 + __ x + 5   Group like terms
= __ x^2 + __ x + __   Combine like terms

b)

=   Group like terms
=   Combine like terms

c)

d)

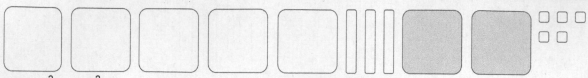

5. Sketch the algebra tiles.

Simplify by combining like terms.

a) $5x + 5 - 8x + 3$

= $5x$ − ___ + __ + 3   Group like terms.
= __ x + __   Combine like terms.

b) $2x^2 + 3x - 4x^2 + 6x$

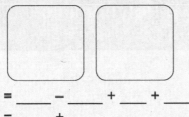

= ____ − ____ + ___ + ___   Group like terms.
= ___ + ____   Combine like terms.

c) $5 + 4x + 3x^2 - 2x$

6. Combine like terms to simplify.

a) $-8 + 4x + 7x + 6$ Group like terms.
= __x + __x − __ + __   Combine like terms.
= __x − __

Tip

Don't forget to check the sign of each term.

b) $5x^2 - 3x + 2 - 5x - 6x^2$ Group like terms.
= ___ − ___ − ___ − ___ + __   Combine like terms.
=

c) $2x^2 + 9 + 9x + 5x^2$

7. Simplify each expression.

a) $6x + 7 + 2x - 3$ **b)** $7x^2 - 4x - 9x^2 - 2x$

Quick Review

To add the polynomials $3x^2 + 2x - 3$ and $x^2 - 5x + 4$, we write
$(3x^2 + 2x - 3) + (x^2 - 5x + 4)$.

Use algebra tiles to model each polynomial.

$3x^2 + 2x - 3$ $x^2 - 5x + 4$

Group and combine like terms.

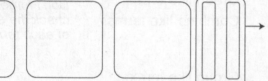

We can add polynomials by grouping like terms and simplifying.

$(3x^2 + 2x - 3) + (x^2 - 5x + 4)$	Remove the brackets.
$= 3x^2 + 2x - 3 + x^2 - 5x + 4$	Group like terms.
$= 3x^2 + x^2 + 2x - 5x - 3 + 4$	Combine like terms.
$= 4x^2 - 3x + 1$	

Or we can add polynomials vertically.

Align like terms.	$3x^2 + 2x - 3$
	$\underline{+\ x^2 - 5x + 4}$
Combine like terms.	$4x^2 - 3x + 1$

Practice

1. Circle the polynomial sum that represents
each set of tiles.

 ········· **Hint**

*Make sure to
combine like terms.*

a)

$2x^2 + 1x + 4$

$5x^2 - 4$

$6x^2 + 8x - 8$

b)

$4x^2 - 5$

$4x + 5$

$8x + 10$

c)

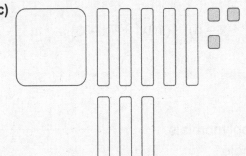  

$-4x^2 + 2x + 1$

$4x^2 + 8x + 7$

$-5x^2 + 16x - 4$

2. Add. Use algebra tiles if it helps.

a) $(2x + 3) + (-4x + 4)$ Remove the brackets.
     $= 2x + 3$ _____   Group like terms.
     $= 2x$ _____ $+ 3$ ___   Combine like terms.
     $=$ _____ $+$ __

b) $(8x - 5) + (x - 6)$ Remove the brackets.
     $= 8x - 5 +$ _____   Group like terms.
     $=$ Combine like terms.
     $=$

c) $(9x - 6) + (7 - 9x)$ d) $(3 - 9x) + (x^2 + 3x - 4)$

3. Add vertically.

a) $(-x - 2) + (8x + 6)$
    $-x - 2$ Align like terms.
    $+ 8x + 6$ Combine like terms.

b) $(8x^2 - 3x + 1) + (3x^2 - 5x + 7)$
    $8x^2 - 3x + 1$ Align like terms.
    $+ 3x^2 - 5x + 7$ Combine like terms.

c) $(4 - 6x + 3x^2) + (2 - 3x + 4x^2)$ d) $(7x^2 + x - 5) + (10x^2 + 7x - 3)$

4. The perimeter of this rectangle is represented by polynomials. Write an expression for the perimeter of the rectangle.

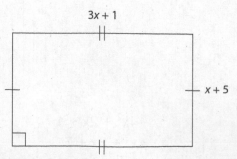

$P = \ell + w + \ell + w$
    $= ($_____$) + ($_____$) + ($_____$) + ($_____$)$ Remove the brackets.
    $=$ Group like terms.
    $=$ Combine like terms.
    $=$

The perimeter of the rectangle is _____.

5. Write an expression for the perimeter of the following figures.

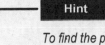 **Hint**

To find the perimeter, find the sum of the sides.

a)

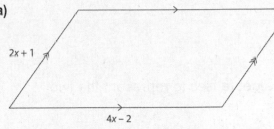

$P = ($_____$) + ($_____$) + ($_____$) + ($_____$)$

The perimeter of the parallelogram is _____.

b)

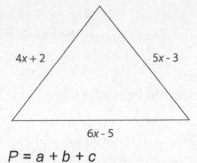

4x + 2

5x - 3

6x - 5

$P = a + b + c$

Tip

To make sure you have included all sides in the perimeter, start at a point and draw around the figure with your pencil.

The perimeter of the triangle is _____.

6. Find 2 polynomials with a sum of $5x^2 + 2x - 3$. Show your work.

Tip

You can use algebra tiles to construct the polynomial.

7. Create a polynomial that is added to $3x^2 + 4x + 1$ to get each sum.

Tip

Use algebra tiles to help create the missing polynomial.

a) $5x^2 + 8x + 3$

b) $x^2 + x + 1$

8. The sum of 2 polynomials is $8x^2 + 12x + 2$.
One polynomial is $7x^2 + 8x - 9$.
What is the other polynomial? Show your work.

Quick Review

To subtract a polynomial, we add its opposite.

To simplify $(3x^2 + 2x - 4) - (2x^2 - 5x + 1)$, use algebra tiles to represent the two polynomials.

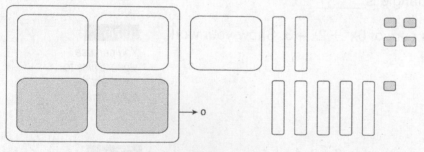

To subtract $2x^2 - 5x + 1$, add the opposite polynomial.
The opposite polynomial is created by changing the signs to the opposite signs.

These tiles represent $(3x^2 + 2x - 4) + (-2x^2 + 5x - 1)$.
Combine the like terms.

The remaining tiles represent $x^2 + 7x - 5$.
So, $(3x^2 + 2x - 4) + (-2x^2 + 5x - 1) = x^2 + 7x - 5$.

We subtract a polynomial by adding its opposite.
Subtract: $(9x^2 - 9x + 11) - (8x^2 + 3x - 1)$

$(9x^2 - 9x + 11) - (8x^2 + 3x - 1)$	Add the opposite.
$= (9x^2 - 9x + 11) + (-8x^2 - 3x + 1)$	Remove the brackets.
$= 9x^2 - 9x + 11 - 8x^2 - 3x + 1$	Group like terms.
$= 9x^2 - 8x^2 - 9x - 3x + 11 + 1$	Combine like terms.
$= x^2 - 12x + 12$	

Practice

1. Show the opposite of each polynomial by sketching the appropriate algebra tiles.

a)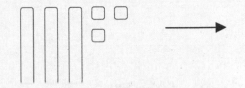

> **Tip**
>
> A zero pair is one grey tile and one white tile of the same size.

b)

2. Simplify. Use algebra tiles if it helps.

a) $(x + 8) - (x + 3)$ Add the opposite.

    $= (x + 8) + ($ _____ $)$ Remove the brackets.

    $= x + 8$ _____   Group like terms.

    $=$ Combine like terms.

    $=$

> **Tip**
>
> Subtracting a negative is like adding a positive.

b) $(4x - 5) - (5x + 3)$ Add the opposite.

    $= (4x - 5) + ($ _____ $)$ Remove the brackets.

    $= 4x - 5$ _____   Group like terms.

    $=$ Combine like terms.

    $=$

3. Simplify.

a) $(2x^2 + 3x - 4) - (4x^2 + 3x - 6)$ Add the opposite.

    $= (2x^2 + 3x - 4) + ($ _____ $)$ Remove the brackets.

    $= 2x^2 + 3x - 4$ _____   Group like terms.

    $= 2x^2$ ____ $+ 3x$ ____ $- 4$ ___   Combine like terms.

    $=$ ____ $+$ __

b) $(4x^2 + 6x - 4) - (x^2 - 8x + 2)$ Add the opposite.

    $= (4x^2 + 6x - 4) + ($ _____ $)$ Remove the brackets.

    $= 4x^2 + 6x - 4$ _____   Group like terms.

    $=$ Combine like terms.

    $=$

c) $(x^2 - x - 1) - (x^2 + x + 1)$

d) $(3 + 6x^2 - 7x) - (4x^2 - 8 + 3x)$

4. Simplify. Check your answers by adding.

a) $(3x + 2) - (4x - 8)$

$= (3x + 2)$ _____

b) $(6x^2 - 4x) - (2x^2 + 9x)$

To check, add the difference to the
second polynomial:

$(4x - 8) + ($ _____ $)$

$= 4x - 8$ _____

$=$ _____

The sum is _____ (equal, not equal)
to the first polynomial.
So, the difference is _____
(incorrect, correct).

To check, add the difference to the
second polynomial:

$(2x^2 + 9x) + ($ _____ $)$

$= 2x^2 + 9x$ _____

$=$ _____

The sum is _____ to the first
polynomial.
So, the difference is _____.

c) $(7x^2 - 6x + 4) - (5x^2 + 7x - 9)$

d) $(x^3 - 8 + 3x) - (5x + 3 - 2x^3)$

184

Quick Review

We can use algebra tiles to model the multiplication of a polynomial with a constant term.

To multiply $2(3x + 4)$, construct a rectangle with length $3x + 4$ and width 2.
Fill in the rectangle with algebra tiles.

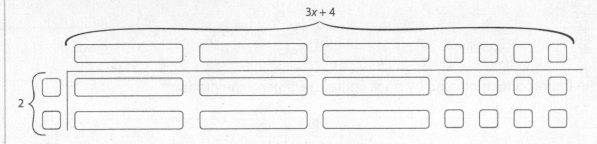

It will take 6 x-tiles and 8 1-tiles to fill in the rectangle.
So, $2(3x + 4) = 6x + 8$

Instead of algebra tiles, we can use a rectangle to model the area.

We divide the rectangle
into two rectangles.
Rectangle A has area: $2(3x) = 6x$
Rectangle B has area: $2(4) = 8$
The total area is: $6x+8$
So, $2(3x + 4) = 6x + 8$

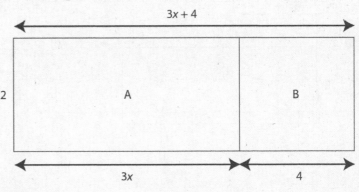

To determine $2(3x + 4)$ using pencil and
paper, multiply each term in the brackets
by the term outside the brackets.
In this case, we multiply by the constant term 2. ◄·········
This is called *expanding*.

$2(3x + 4) = 2(3x) + 2(4)$
$\qquad = 6x + 8$

This illustrates the **distributive law**.

Hint
A constant term is a term without a variable.

Practice

1. Use algebra tiles to determine each product. Sketch the tiles you used.

   a) $3(2x + 4)$

   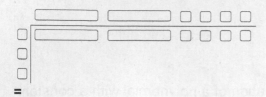

   =

   b) $2(2x + 1)$

   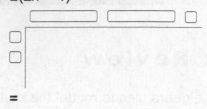

   =

   c) $5(2x + 1)$

   =

   d) $3(x + 6)$

   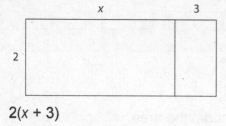

   =

2. Write the product modelled by each figure. Determine the product.

   a)

   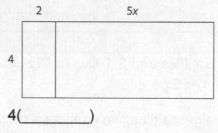

   $2(x + 3)$
   = ____ + ____

   b)

   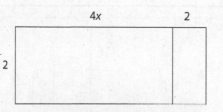

   $4(\underline{\hspace{2cm}})$
   =

   c)

   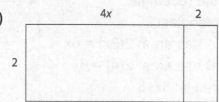

   d)

   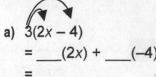

3. Expand.

   a) $3(2x - 4)$
   = ____$(2x)$ + ____(-4)
   =

   b) $3(-2x + 4)$
   = _____ + ____
   =

Tip
The arrows represent the distributive law.

   c) $-3(2x - 4)$

   d) $-3(-2x + 4)$

e) $-7(3x^2 - 4x + 3)$

f) $8(2x^2 - 3x + 5)$

4. a) Expand: $230(56x^2 + 3x)$

b) Explain how you found the result.

_____

5. Beverly is making a square pen for her pigs.
Each side has length $3x + 4$, where x represents the number of pigs.
Find the perimeter.

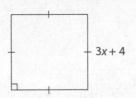

$3x + 4$

$P = 4\ell$
$P = (4)(\underline{\hspace{2cm}})$
$\quad = (4)(\underline{\hspace{1.5cm}}) + (4)(\underline{\hspace{1cm}})$
$\quad =$

The perimeter of the pig pen is

_____.

6. Gary wants to paint his bedroom. He needs to calculate the perimeter before he knows how much paint to buy. Find the perimeter.

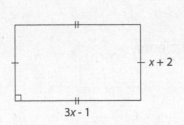

$x + 2$

$3x - 1$

$P = 2\ell + 2w$
$P = 2(\underline{\hspace{2cm}}) + 2(\underline{\hspace{1.5cm}})$

The perimeter of Gary's room is

_____.

7. June is looking at quilts online. Each quilt is made by sewing together pieces of fabric. The quilts can be made any dimension, but they are all square. Each side has length $2x - 3$, where x represents the number of pieces of fabric.
June wants to know the perimeter of the quilt.

$P = 2\ell + 2w$

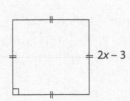

$2x - 3$

The perimeter of the quilt is

_____.

Quick Review

A **monomial** is a polynomial with one term.
Here are some monomials: $3x$, -9, $-6x^2$, $-3x^3$

Algebra tiles can be used to multiply some monomials.

To determine $(2x)(3x)$, draw two sides of a rectangle whose length is $3x$ and whose width is $2x$.

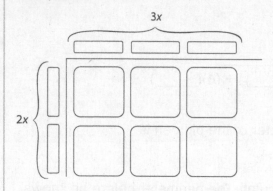

Fill in the rectangle with algebra tiles.
It will take 6 x^2-tiles to fill in the rectangle.
So, $(2x)(3x) = 6x^2$

In the monomials $2x$ and $3x$, the numbers 2 and 3 are coefficients.
To multiply the two monomials,
multiply the coefficients: $(3)(2) = 6$
multiply the variables: $(x)(x) = x^2$
So, $(3x)(2x) = 6x^2$

Using algebra tiles to model multiplication only works when multiplying positive x-tiles.
To multiply higher powers, we must use pencil-and-paper methods.

To multiply $(2x^2)(3x)$,

multiply the coefficients: $(2)(3) = 6$
multiply the variables: $(x^2)(x) = (x)(x)(x)$
$\qquad\qquad\qquad\qquad\qquad\quad = x^3$

So, $(2x^2)(3x) = 6x^3$

Practice

1. Use algebra tiles to find each product.
   Sketch the tiles you need.

   a) $(4x)(2x)$

   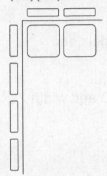

   So, $(4x)(2x) =$ _____

   b) $(2x)(2x)$

   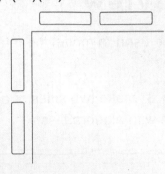

   So, $(2x)(2x) =$ _____

2. Use pencil and paper to multiply the following.

   a) $(4x)(2x^2)$
   $(4)(2) =$ ___   Multiply the coefficients
   $(x)(x^2) =$ ___   Multiply the variables.

   So, $(4x)(3x^2) =$ ___

   b) $(3x)(8x^2)$

   So, $(3x)(8x^2) =$ _____

3. Multiply.

   a) $(4x)(6x)$
   $(4)(6) =$ ___
   $(x)(x) =$ ___

   So, $(4x)(6x) =$ _____

   b) $(-4x)(6x)$
   $(\_)(\_) =$ ___
   $(\_)(\_) =$ ___

   So, $(-4x)(6x) =$ _____

   c) $(-4x)(-6x)$

   So, $(-4x)(-6x) =$ _____

4. William got the following question wrong on his homework.
   Explain where he made his mistake.

   $(-2x)(-4x) = -8x^2$

   _____

5. Multiply.

   a) $(-5x)(-6x)$

   b) $(-4x)(-2x^2)$

   So, $(-5x)(-6x) =$ _____

   So, $(-4x)(-2x2) =$ _____

Quick Review

Algebra tiles can be used to model the multiplication of some polynomials and monomials.

To multiply $2x(4x + 3)$ make two sides of a rectangle with length $4x + 3$ and width $2x$.
Fill in the rectangle with algebra tiles.

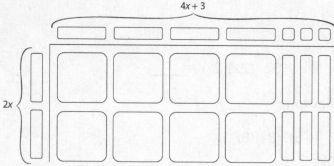

It takes 8 x^2-tiles and 6 x-tiles to fill in the rectangle.
So, $2x(4x + 3) = 8x^2 + 6x$

You can also determine the product using an area model.
Sketch a rectangle with width $2x$ and length $4x + 3$.
The area of the rectangle is: $2x(4x + 3)$
Divide the rectangle into 2 rectangles.

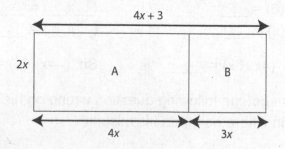

Rectangle A has area: $(2x)(4x) = 8x^2$
Rectangle B has area: $(2x)(3) = 6x$
The total area is: $8x^2 + 6x$
So, $2x(4x + 3) = 8x^2 + 6x$

Multiply $2x(4x + 3)$ using the distributive law.
Multiply each term in the brackets by the term outside the brackets.

$2x(4x + 3) = (2x)(4x) + (2x)(3)$
$\qquad\qquad = 8x^2 + 6x$

Practice

1. Use algebra tiles to expand. Sketch the tiles you need.

   a) $3x(x + 3)$

   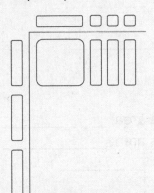

   So, $3x(x + 3) =$ _____

   b) $2x(3x + 1)$

   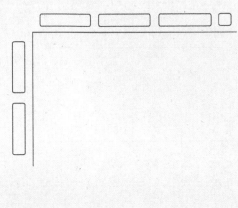

   So, $2x(3x + 1) =$ _____

   c) $4x(5x + 7)$

   So, $4x(5x + 7) =$ _____

   d) $2x(2x + 6)$

   So, $2x(2x + 6) =$ _____

2. Write the product modelled by the area of each rectangle. Determine the product.

a)

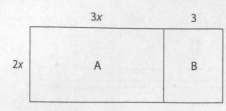

Rectangle A has area: (2*x*) _____ = _____
Rectangle B has area: (2*x*) _____ = _____
The total area is: _____

So, 2*x*(3*x* + 3) = _____.

b)

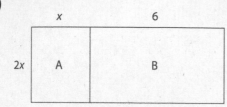

Rectangle A has area: _____
Rectangle B has area: _____
The total area is: _____

So, 2*x*(*x* + 6) = _____.

c)

Rectangle A has area: _____
Rectangle B has area: _____
The total area is: _____

So, 6*x*(6*x* + 5) = _____.

3. Expand. You may find it helpful to use algebra tiles.

a) 3*x*(*x* + 2)

= (3*x*)(____) + (3*x*)(____)

= _____

b) 4*x*(2*x* + 3)

= _____ + _____

=

> **Tip**
> *Don't forget to multiply the coefficient and the variable*

c) *x*(8*x* + 10)

d) 7*x*(6*x* + 4)

e) 2*x*²(*x* + 4)

f) *x*(2*x* − 8)

g) *x*(6*x*² + 12*x*)

h) 6*x*(−5*x* − 4)

4. Expand.

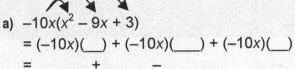

a) $-10x(x^2 - 9x + 3)$

$\quad = (-10x)(\underline{\quad}) + (-10x)(\underline{\quad}) + (-10x)(\underline{\quad})$

$\quad = \underline{\qquad} + \underline{\qquad} - \underline{\quad}$

b) $5x(3x^2 - 3x + 7)$

$\quad = \underline{\quad}\,\underline{\qquad} + \underline{\quad}\,\underline{\qquad} + \underline{\quad}\,\underline{\qquad}$

$\quad =$

c) $-3x(-3x^2 + 3x)$

d) $4x(-8x^2 + 2x - 4)$

5. Fiona got the following question wrong on her test.
Explain what she did wrong. What is the correct answer?

$x(x + 3) = 2x + 3$

_____

_____

6. Determine the area.

a)

9x + 4

4x

$A = \ell\, w$

$A = \underline{\qquad}\ \underline{\quad}$

$\quad = \underline{\qquad\qquad}$

The area of the rectangle is _____.

b)

4x - 3

A

3x

B   2x + 3

3x

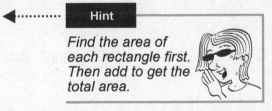

Hint

Find the area of
each rectangle first.
Then add to get the
total area.

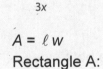

$A = \ell\, w$

Rectangle A:

Total area:

$= \underline{\qquad} + \underline{\qquad}$

Rectangle B:

The area of the figure is _____.

Solving Equations with More than One Variable Term

Quick Review

We can use a balance strategy to solve equations.

We perform the same operations on each side of the equation until we are left with the variable on one side of the equals sign and the constant term on the other side of the equals sign.

Solve: $7 + 2x = -2x - 9$
Check the solution.

$$7 + 2x = -2x - 9$$
$$7 + 2x + 2x = -2x - 9 + 2x$$
$$7 + 4x = -9$$
$$7 + 4x - 7 = -9 - 7$$
$$4x = -16$$
$$\frac{4x}{4} = -\frac{16}{4}$$
$$x = -4$$

To remove $-2x$, add $2x$ to each side.
Simplify.
To remove 7, add -7 to each side.

To isolate x, divide by 4.

To check the solution, substitute $x = -4$ in each side of the equation.

$$\text{L.S.} = 7 + 2x \qquad\qquad \text{R.S.} = -2x - 9$$
$$= 7 + 2(-4) \qquad\qquad = -2(-4) - 9$$
$$= -1 \qquad\qquad\qquad = -1$$

Since the left side equals the right side, the solution is correct.

Practice

1. Solve. Explain your steps.

a) $4x + 9 = x$

    $4x + 9 \rule{1cm}{0.4pt} = x \rule{1cm}{0.4pt}$

    $\rule{1cm}{0.4pt} = \rule{1cm}{0.4pt}$

    $\rule{1cm}{0.4pt} = \rule{1cm}{0.4pt}$

    $x = \rule{1cm}{0.4pt}$

To remove $4x$, add ____ to both sides.
Simplify.
To isolate x, divide by ____.

◄············· | Hint |

You have to do the same thing to both sides.

b) $-6x = 7x + 26$

To remove _____ add _____ to both sides.
Simplify.
To isolate x, divide by _____

c) $8x - 4 = -2x + 16$

2. Solve and check each equation.

a) $-6x + 12 = -2x + 16$
$-6x + 12$ _____ $= -2x + 16$ _____

To remove _____, add _____ to both sides
Simplify.
To remove _____, add _____ to both sides.
Simplify.
To isolate x, divide by _____.

L.S. $= -6x + 12$
    $= -6$ _____ $+ 12$
    $=$ _____ $+ 12$
    $=$ _____

R.S. $= -2x + 16$
    $= -2$ _____ $+ 16$
    $=$ _____ $+ 16$
    $=$ _____

b) $-8x + 17 = -3x - 8$

L.S. =

R.S. =

Tip

Get into the habit of always checking your answers.

195

c) $8x + 1 = x + 15$

L.S. =   R.S. =

d) $8x - 6 - 2x = 9 + 5x$

L.S. =   R.S. =

4. William was away from class today. How would you explain to William how to solve $10 - 5x = 2x + 3$? What is the answer?

_____

_____

_____

_____

Hint

Start by multiplying each term in the brackets by the term outside the brackets.

5. Solve and explain your steps.

        $5(x + 3) = 15$

In Your Words

Here are some of the important mathematical words of this unit.
Build your own glossary by recording definitions and examples here. The first one is done for you.

polynomial _an expression with one or more terms_

For example, $7x^2$, $4x + 5$, and $4x^2 + 3x - 2$ are polynomials.

term

variable

coefficient

constant term

like terms

zero pair

List other mathematical words you need to know.

Chapter Review

7.1 **1.** Write a simplified expression for each group of tiles.

a)

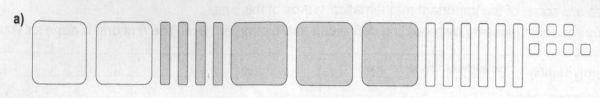

_____

b)

_____

2. Write 3 like terms for 4x.

Explain why they are like terms

_____

_____

7.2 **3.** Add. Use algebra tiles if it helps.

a) $(4x + 4) + (2x + 2)$

b) $(5x^2 - 9x + 7) + (4x^2 - 7x + 2)$

4. Determine the perimeter of the triangle.

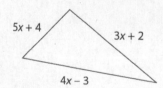

The perimeter of the triangle is _____.

5. Simplify. Use algebra tiles if it helps.

    a) $(8x + 3) - (3x - 6)$ **b)** $(5x^2 + 7x - 4) - (6x^2 + 9x - 3)$

    c) $(3x^2 - 5x + 2) - (4x^2 - x - 5)$ **d)** $(6x^2 + 2x) - (-2x^2 - 3x)$

6. Expand.

    a) $5(3x + 7)$ **b)** $-8(9x + 2)$

    c) $3(x^2 - 2x + 7)$ **d)** $4(2x^2 + 4)$

7. Jimmy is helping Kaila with her homework. Kaila says that $3(x + 4) = 3x + 4$. What is Kaila's mistake?

_____

_____

8. Multiply.

    a) $(x)(6x)$ **b)** $(4x)(2x^2)$

    c) $(-3)(4x)$ **d)** $(x^2)(-3x)$

9. Expand.

a) $3x(6x + 2)$

b) $2x(11x^2 + 6x)$

c) $2x(5x^2 - 3x + 4)$

d) $-3x(7x^2 + 4x - 8)$

10. Determine the area of the shaded portion of the rectangle.

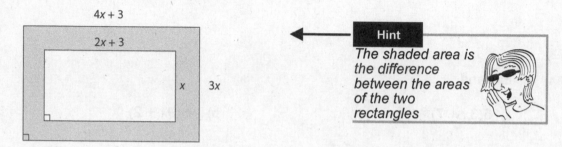

Hint

The shaded area is the difference between the areas of the two rectangles

$A = \ell w$

The area of the shaded portion of the rectangle is _____.

11. Solve each equation.

a) $4x + 8 = 2x$

b) $x + 9 = 3 - x$